PREFACE

The painting must have been exhibited at the Royal Academy during Queen Victoria's reign, or be a study for or replica of a painting which was.

This was and is the basic rule which has governed the formation of this collection almost since its inception. The only flexibility that has been permitted is an allowance of two years on each end of Victoria's reign.

Why Victorian painting? *Forbes'* interest began with my purchase of Graham Reynolds's *Victorian Painting* in a Bermuda bookstore in 1969. The dazzling four-color reproduction of some of the cream of nineteenth-century Britannia's academic output fired my imagination, and prompted the purchase of what was then the only other lavishly illustrated book on this long-ridiculed or ignored genre, Jeremy Maas's *Victorian Painters*. The following summer it was not the Turner galleries which drew me to the Tate, but William Powell Frith's *Derby Day*.

Forbes Magazine, in fact, already had a major Frith (see No. 17), part of an eclectic assortment of paintings assembled for the Magazine by my father in the '50s and early '60s. The Magazine's Collection included numerous pictures but, prior to 1969, its most important collections were of Fabergé, Presidential Autographs, and Kinetic Art. Paintings moved dramatically to the forefront, however, in 1969 when a number of major paintings, including Rubens's *Cupid Supplicating Jupiter's Consent to his Marriage to Psyche,* Gauguin's *Les Enfants dans la Rue,* and Toulouse-Lautrec's *Le Polisseur,* were added to the Magazine's Collection.

It was the growing number of acquisitions in the Impressionist field that prompted my suggestion that the Magazine would do better to collect a less-sought-after aspect of the nineteenth century. Why pay huge prices for less than first-rank works of a school at the peak of its popularity, when major examples of Victorian painting were fetching less than the sales tax on a third-rate Pissarro? Using a heavy dose of the hard sell, which eventually brought me to my present position as an advertising salesman at *Forbes,* I was able to persuade my father that the Magazine could assemble the "best" collection of Victorian pictures on this side of the Atlantic for the price of a lovely, but relatively unimportant, Monet *Waterlilies* which hung in his office.

First a very large list of Victorian artists and their "specialties" was drawn up. Then as it became apparent that pictures which had been exhibited at the Royal Academy were often the most splendid examples which came on the market, the "rule" noted earlier was put into effect. The importance of the Academy's annual exhibitions meant that pictures exhibited there were often the subject of much contemporary critical commentary, ranging from the Olympian opinions of John Ruskin to the satirical barbs of the editors of *Punch;* from the precious comments of William Thackeray to the affluent amateur-turned-art-critic opinions of Francis Turner Palgrave. This reservoir of Victorian views made it possible to determine which artists were the most highly regarded in their own time and therefore most desirable to include in the collection.

A list of fifteen "most wanted" and seventeen "wanted" artists was eventually drawn up. Two weeks before this catalogue went to press, the purchase of George Frederick Watts's *Orpheus and Eurydice* (see No. 67) completed the "most wanted" list.

Purely personal preference has swelled the list of thirty-two artists included in the "wanted" and "most wanted" lists to the fifty-eight represented in this catalogue. It has also resulted in the gross over-representation of the works of Laslett John Pott (see Nos. 53, 54, 55), but I never could determine what constitutes the most desirable and important work by an artist as obscure as Laslett Pott. Personal preference has always had to be confined to the Academy rule, but with over 100,000 works having been exhibited at the Royal Academy during Queen Victoria's reign, this restriction has not really been overwhelming.

Although we long ago exceeded the budget dictated by the since-discarded Monet, and while there are those who might dispute that *Forbes'* is the best collection of Victorian paintings in this hemisphere, I have never regretted the decision to collect mid- and late nineteenth-century academic British pictures, though my father's enthusiasm might be described as restrained or rueful. The growth of interest in the period has given the Collection a vitality and excitement well beyond what anyone, least of all myself, envisioned just five short years ago.

D1530068

CHRISTOPHER FORBES

CONTENTS

THE VICTORIAN ROYAL ACADEMY

Queen Victoria reigned from 1837 until 1901. Those dates define the Victorian period, although the word "Victorian" has taken on many additional meanings, most of which, until recently, have tended to be pejorative. Give or take a year or two, all the pictures in this exhibition were painted between 1837 and 1901, and they constitute a gathering of what we might reasonably describe as typically Victorian art. However, they are not just typically Victorian pictures; the raison d'être of this exhibition is that the works in it either are pictures which were shown in exhibitions of the Royal Academy or are directly related as sketches for, or replicas, of exhibited pictures. This exhibition does not focus upon the major Victorian artists — in fact, it does not include all of them — but it does show what the Victorians saw when they went to exhibitions. Many of the artists represented had great Victorian reputations; others were little noticed in their own lifetimes: together, their works present a cross section of what was exhibited at the Royal Academy during the sixty-four years that Victoria ruled.[1] This introductory essay is about that institution, upon whose walls the pictures in this exhibition first were seen.

In November of 1768 a group of English artists addressed a petition to King George III soliciting his protection for a society which was to have two principal purposes: "establishing a well-regulated School or Academy of Design, for the use of students in the Arts, and an Annual Exhibition, open to all artists of distinguished merit, where they may offer their performances to public inspection, and acquire that degree of reputation and encouragement which they shall be deemed to deserve."[2] The King gave his approval, and by the end of the year the Royal Academy was formally established. In the following April the Academy opened an exhibition of one hundred and thirty-six works in its first premises in Somerset House, and so began a series of annual exhibitions which has continued unbroken to the present day. In the nineteenth century the Academy moved its home twice: in 1837 to a new building in Trafalgar Square which it shared with the infant National Gallery, and then in 1868, when the National Gallery needed more space, to its own building, Burlington House in Piccadilly, where it still remains. Each move provided more exhibition space, so by the end of the nineteenth century the average number of works in an annual exhibition approached two thousand.[3] Although there were rival exhibitions, throughout the nineteenth century the Royal Academy was always the great annual exhibition of contemporary works of art in the British Isles, and the great increase in the number of works exhibited is a reflection not only of the Academy's ability to accommodate them but also, and more significantly, of the important position held by its exhibitions in the lives of most English artists, and indeed in English life. In the 1880s and 1890s between 350,000 and 400,000 people regularly attended the exhibitions; the Private View and the Annual Dinner before the opening were two of the most prestigious social events of the English year; and the dates of the exhibition, from the beginning of May to the beginning of August, defined the fasionable London "Season."[4]

The operations of the Royal Academy have remained much the same since the eighteenth century. It was and is a self-perpetuating body, whose members are elected for life. Originally there were forty Academicians; this number was raised to forty-two in 1853 to allow two engravers, who had previously been excluded, to be full Academicians. In addition, the Academy has a category of Associate members who share most of the privileges of membership and from whom the full members are elected. Through most of the nineteenth century the number of Associates was limited to twenty, but in 1866 in response to public criticism that the Royal Academy was too exclusive, and to ensuing governmental pressure, the rules were revised to allow an unlimited number of Associates with twenty as the minimum number. However, only in 1876 were any additional Associates elected. Currently there are around thirty. Two women artists were founding members of the Academy in 1768, and there have been women members since 1900, but no women were elected to either full or associate membership in the nineteenth century.

Although the Academy's membership was limited, the exhibitions were open to all artists, in accordance with the original petition of 1768. In the Victorian period, pictures painted by members or associates were only a fraction of the works on view. In an exhibition at Burlington House entries in all media were included by eight hundred or one thousand different artists. This sounds remarkably inclusive, but normally around five thousand artists submitted as many as twelve thousand works, so a screening process had to take place.[5] Members and Associates had the right to exhibit eight works, although few, other than portrait painters, exhibited that many. Outsiders could also submit eight works, but these had to undergo the scrutiny of the Council, an annually rotating group of Academicians. The installation of the exhibition was the responsibility of the Hanging Committee, consisting of three (or after 1871, five) painters, a sculptor, and an architect. As pictures usually hung frame-to-frame from floor to ceiling, the power of the members of this committee to put a work either in a conspicuous position or out of sight was as important as that of the Council to select or reject. As there never were five thousand artists of professional competence working in the British Isles at any one time, the Council's main role was to weed out the obviously incompetent works sent in annually by armies of amateur artists, and the Council delegated to the Hanging Committee the responsibility of including or rejecting the many works which it placed in the category of doubtful. The Academy as a whole had no policy of opposing progressive tendencies in painting, such as Pre-Raphaelitism, but a conservative member of the Hanging Committee did have considerable power to help his friends and hurt his enemies. Although there were on occasion rejections of major pictures (for example, Whistler's White Girl was rejected in 1862), the most frequent protest was not about outright rejection of a work, but about its being hung in a spot where nobody could, or would, see it. Younger artists and other outsiders frequently and legitimately complained that the best places "on the line" were taken year after year by members of the Academy.

"The line" was a ledge two inches deep which ran around the galleries in Somerset House and Trafalgar Square at a height of eight feet or slightly more above the floor. All large portraits and other pictures with life-sized or over life-sized figures had to be placed above this ledge; it, in fact, was there to provide support for the weight of the largest works. A picture hung "on the line" was immediately below the ledge, and hence the top of its frame was eight feet from the floor. This was the ideal position for a picture to be seen, at or just above eye level, whereas a picture "skied" way above the line could be literally invisible. The exclusion of very large pictures from the best positions in the exhibition had the effect of encouraging artists to think and work on a small scale.[6] Although older English painters had frequently painted huge pictures, by the second quarter of the nineteenth century only very exceptional pictures had figures of life-size or larger.[7] The characteristic early or mid-Victorian picture is of moderate size (six feet or less in its largest dimension) and painted with precise detail which demands to be examined closely. Other factors also discouraged artists from working on a monumental scale,[8] but since artists made their reputations by having their pictures seen in exhibitions, it made sense for them to paint works that could be seen in the best possible circumstances. When the Academy moved to Burlington House in 1869 the line was abolished; large pictures could be hung at eye level, and soon large pictures started to come back into fashion.

Although the English Royal Academy was partly modeled on the French *Académie Royale,* which had been founded over a century earlier, the situation of the English artist was very different from that of his French counterpart. In England, unlike France, there was no tradition of munificent royal or state patronage of the arts, nor was there any significant patronage from the church. The French *Académie,* as it was given definitive shape under Louis XIV, was supported by the government, and it existed first of all to guarantee the existence of a community of artists capable of providing decorations for the royal palaces and other public buildings. Before 1789 the *Directeur général des bâtiments* held ultimate authority over the arts; after the Revolution things were reorganized, but state patronage and state control remained paramount. In England artists shaped the Royal Academy to meet their own needs, and, although they sought and received Royal recognition, they kept control of the Academy firmly in their own hands. In France exhibitions, or *Salons,* were only incidental to the functioning of the *Académie;* during periods of the eighteenth century they were not held at all, and through much of the nineteenth they were held only biennially. In England, on the other hand, from the beginning the annual exhibition was of essential and central importance. The income from admissions was sufficient to give financial independence to the Academy, which consequently, despite its dominant position in the English art world, has remained a private body, subject to outside

pressure, but not to outside control. And for the individual artist, who could not count on commissions from church or state, the exhibition was to be the prime means of finding patrons and selling pictures.

Selling pictures is, of course, the most obvious and direct way by which artists can make a living. Before the nineteenth century most artists depended on commissions; a patron, private or public, employed an artist to paint a picture to fulfill specific requirements. In England, through the eighteenth century, portraiture was by far the most lucrative branch of painting, and portraitists, by the nature of their art, had to work on commission. The eighteenth-century landscape painter also regularly worked to order, producing views of country houses for their owners or overdoors and other decorative works to fit specific rooms. Regular exhibitions were to change this pattern. Artists could paint what they wanted, or what they thought would sell, send it to exhibition, and hope there to interest a buyer. Eighteenth-century patrons came to the artist and told him what they wanted; nineteenth-century patrons saw pictures exhibited and purchased what they liked. Also, exhibitions, by making large numbers of works of art available to the public, helped to create a market which had not existed before. Prior to the formation of the Royal Academy patronage of the arts had primarily been aristocratic, but already in the eighteenth century the industrial revolution was creating a new and powerfully wealthy middle class. In the Victorian period there still were aristocratic patrons; Charles Eastlake, who lived for over a decade in Rome, painted many pictures for lords on the Grand Tour in the eighteenth-century fashion. But the great Victorian collectors were manufacturers, shipowners, and financiers, who had often risen from humble beginnings. These men had very different backgrounds from the lordly patrons of the previous century. They had not grown up in ancestral homes hung with Dutch and Italian paintings and family portraits by Van Dyck; nor had their ideas of what pictures should be been established by a visit to Italy on the Grand Tour. Their tastes were shaped by what they saw exhibited at the Royal Academy's exhibitions. In many cases, they probably would not have bought pictures at all if the Royal Academy had not broken down traditional closed circles of patronage by presenting well-publicized and well-attended exhibitions of works most of which were for sale. They came to the exhibitions without firmly formed preconceptions based on earlier art, and they were fully prepared to see the progress of contemporary art as yet one more supreme achievement of Victorian England, surpassing all that had been done in the past.

Because of the rapid expansion of middle-class wealth in the nineteenth century, there were plenty of potential purchasers, and the system worked quite successfully, monetarily at least, for the artists, many of whom made huge fortunes. It is probably safe to say that during the Victorian period more artists made more money than in any other period before or after. The system also worked to give artists independence to choose what they painted. Their main concern was how a work would look in an exhibition, not if it would please an individual patron. Although the hundreds of thousands of people who annually attended the exhibition of the Royal Academy did not all buy pictures by any means, they were part of the market for the engraving after a popular picture; and the copyright to a picture (i.e. the right to make and sell an engraving after it) was often worth as much as the picture itself. For example, William Powell Frith, whose *Derby Day* (Tate Gallery) created a sensation at the Royal Academy exhibition of 1858, sold the painting to a private patron for £1500, but he sold the copyright to a dealer for another £1500 and the right to send it on a world-wide exhibition tour for an additional £750 (To have some sense of what these figures mean, we should probably consider a mid-nineteenth-century pound the equivalent of twenty-five to thirty of our dollars). Since a very large public could afford to buy prints, and an even larger one could pay a few pennies to see a work exhibited, widespread popularity could yield the artist far more than satisfaction for his ego. To meet the demand of the more affluent, an artist might also paint several replicas of a particularly popular work.

Not all astists achieved such broadly-based popularity as Frith, and not all wanted it. For the Pre-Raphaelites, and for many critics, the success of Frith was based on a too deliberate appeal to popular taste. As Ruskin wrote, *Derby Day* was "necessarily, because popular, stooping and restricted."[9] The word "philistine" as we normally use it was introduced into the English language by two Victorian highbrows, Thomas Carlyle and Matthew Arnold, and it was soon applied to extremely popular artists such as Frith or Edwin Landseer or John Everett Millais in his later years. In the view of some more progressive artists, the Royal Academy exhibitions by the middle of the nineteenth century had degenerated into gargantuan extravaganzas which no longer provided a suitable place to show serious works of art. Dante Gabriel Rossetti never exhibited there; Edward Burne-Jones, even though he was constantly wooed by the Academicians and even made an Associate member, exhibited only one painting there, claiming that his work "would look strange and without reason on the Academy walls," and he eventually resigned.[10] The Grosvenor Gallery, which opened in 1877, and its successor the New Gallery were created to provide a more sympathetic place of exhibition for artists like Burne-Jones. In 1886 a group of younger artists, all of whom had studied in France, founded the New English Art Club where they could exhibit their works rather than send them to the Academy.

These developments were paralleled in France, where a *Salon des Indépendants* as well as smaller exhibitions such as those of the Impressionists provided alternatives to the official *Salon*. In both countries we can see a growing split between certain artists, who usually thought of themselves as an *avant-garde* and whose pictures were appreciated by a limited audience, and the official or semiofficial artistic establishment. But there were fundamental differences. The Royal Academy was a more flexible institution than the *Salon*. It was ready to

bend with the wind: to adjust its standards to accommodate changing tastes and new developments. The Academy did not reject Burne-Jones; Burne-Jones rejected the Academy. In France, the *Salon* underwent several reformations, notably in the manner by which pictures were selected or rejected, but it remained the route to official patronage in the form of commissions for public buildings or purchases for the Luxembourg, Versailles, and various provincial museums. The pattern of state purchases was not unchanging either, but through the century the state did continue to encourage monumental paintings for public places, the great *machines* which set the standards for *Salon* paintings. In England, with the significant but solitary exception of the program for decorating the newly built Houses of Parliament in the 1840s and 1850s, there was no important public patronage. The Royal Academy was left a fund by the sculptor Francis Chantrey to buy British art, and beginning in 1877 it normally used it to make purchases from the Academy exhibitions. These purchases, however, were generally of the most popular pictures; instead of leading public taste or maintaining standards, the Academy as an institution encouraged artists to give the public what it wanted.

The Academy also had the opportunity to affect the nature of the works exhibited on its walls by the education it gave to young artists in its schools, which through most of the nineteenth century constituted far and away the most important place in the British Isles for the training of painters and sculptors. In this role the Academy was the equivalent of the French *Ecole des Beaux-Arts,*[11] but it was a very different institution, and the substantial differences between a characteristic picture in an Academy exhibition and one in the *Salon* were in good part the results of differing *curricula* which prepared artists to do different things. These *curricula* bring us back to the contrast between state-supported institutions, which existed to serve the state, and a private organization, which served the artists. The French system was built around a series of competitions, culminating in the *concours* for the *Prix-de-Rome*, the winners of which spent several years in Rome at government expense. Although a *Prix-de-Rome* for landscape was established in 1817, the main goal of all this was to train history painters, who could carry on a tradition of providing monumental pictures for public commissions. In England, in the Royal Academy Schools there were competitions, and there were grants for travel abroad, but these were given irregularly (for example, no grants were given to painters in the 1870s). There was no equivalent of the French Academy in Rome, and there was no state support nor prospect of state employment for even the most successful student. The artist got the training he wanted from the Academy, but there was no structure of rewards providing incentive to work in a monumental historical style.

In France students were taught to draw at the *Ecole des Beaux-Arts*, but they received instruction in painting and prepared for the *Prix-de-Rome* competition in the *atelier* of an established master. In England the *atelier* system did not exist.

Students both drew and painted at the Royal Academy. There was a Professor of Painting who lectured periodically but did not give instruction in the studio (From 1882 to 1895 the Professor was John Evan Hodgson, the painter of the charming but lightweight *The Queen, God Bless Her!* [see No. 26], which it is perhaps not unfair to cite as an indication of the Academy's less-than-whole-hearted commitment to the grand manner).

Whatever instruction an advanced student received was from a rotating series of Academicians, each of whom served as Visitor in the Life School for a period of one month. This system had the virtue of exposing the aspiring artist to a variety of styles and points of view, but since the Visitors to the Life School were drawn from a spectrum of the Academy's membership, including landscape and animal painters, they could not present a single model which the young artist might hope to emulate. Hence, the system encouraged diversity rather than devotion to a pervasive set of ideals. Also, of course, the English student did not receive consistent criticism and instruction, and he did not have continuous close personal attention from any one master of his craft. As a result, the English artist was less technically competent than his French counterpart. Next to French *Salon* paintings English works usually look somewhat amateurish, less firmly disciplined and less polished. The English realized the shortcomings of their training, and during the second half of the nineteenth century a number of more progressive schools were established which tried to follow the *atelier* system.[12] By and large, however, the prevailing view was that the French paid too great a price to achieve impersonal discipline. The typical response of an English artist who visited the *Salon* in Paris was awe before the technical mastery of the French artists and repugnance for the cold heartlessness of their products. From the opposite perspective, there was not much that a *Salon* painter such as Bouguereau was likely to learn from English art, but a steady stream of more independent figures from Delacroix to the *fin-de-siècle* Symbolists admired the English precisely for an ability to innovate, stylistically and thematically, which had not been pounded out of them by rigid training.[13] While the *Ecole* tried to perpetuate standards of content and craftsmanship formulated in previous centuries, the Academy let them crumble, but there were gains as well as losses in the collapse. English artists such as Frith preceded the Impressionists in painting scenes of modern life by almost twenty years because their educational system was less firmly committed to the shibboleth of high art. At the time that Manet's master, Thomas Couture, was telling Manet that if he did not raise his goals he would be only the Daumier of his time, Frith was a full Academician, phenomenally successful, and providing the lead for countless younger artists.

The predominant mode in Victorian painting was anecdotal genre painting, of which there are numerous examples in this exhibition, including one by Frith (see No. 17). Although Victorian critics recognized the ancestry of this painting in Dutch seventeenth-century art, they considered it, nonetheless, distinctively British, virtually reinvented by Hogarth in the eighteenth century and perfected by David Wilkie. at the beginning of the nineteenth. Everything else came under its sway. The Royal Academy never was able to establish a strict hierarchy of categories of painting, with history painting at the top and genre near the bottom, such as that promulgated by the *Académie Royale,* but the goal of developing a distinguished school of history painting was clearly stated in the *Discourses* of the Academy's first president, Sir Joshua Reynolds. For Reynolds this meant pictures with ennobling subjects drawn from classical sources and a stylistic language based upon the great masters of the sixteenth and seventeenth centuries such as Raphael and Poussin. Although some artists struggled, not too successfully, to live up to these ideals, in wider practice English history painting almost immediately turned to more recent literature for its material. First Shakespeare and Milton, and then gradually a wide range of seventeenth-, eighteenth-, and contemporary nineteenth-century literary sources provided the chief subject matter for the English painters. In the early Victorian period many more paintings were based upon *The Vicar of Wakefield* and *Don Quixote* than upon the *Iliad* and the *Odyssey;* and when the Victorian artist painted actual history he usually depicted a humorous or poignant biographical anecdote from recent times, not a heroic action described by Plutarch. In the language of art-historical categories, these developments reflect the changing ideals of Neo-classicism and Romanticism. Sancho Panza and the good Vicar embodied recognizable human qualities, not timeless virtues, and they could be—in fact, had to be—treated in an easy-going genre-like style rather than with dignified classical formality. Underlying this, however, were the voracious reading habits of nineteenth-century Englishmen. Unlike us, they could not watch television or listen to the radio, and without automobiles and airplanes they were much less mobile. So they stayed home more, and they read far more than we do. The books that everybody read, by Goldsmith, Cervantes, Scott, Dickens, provided a common culture as pervasive as religious belief, and incidents from these books were easily recognizable and comprehensible to virtually every visitor to the Royal Academy exhibitions. If the source was at all obscure it was a common practice to print an appropriate quotation explaining the picture in the exhibition catalogue, and references to several authorities might be cited to provide documentary justification for an artist's treatment of an historical subject. If that did not suffice, the public could count upon the critics to explain complicated subject matter. Rarely did a picture stand alone as an isolated visual experience. Pictures told stories, illustrated literature, provided information. They were full of references to things outside themselves, and they were seen by an audience which was prepared to understand those references. After the middle of the century artists started to invent their own stories instead of illustrating themes from literature (*The Awakening Conscience* by Holman Hunt, exhibited in 1854, is the classic example), and by the 1880s and 1890s they were exhibiting "problem pictures" with deliberately ambiguous titles which invited the audience to invent a narrative to fit the situation depicted.[14] Although, in a sense, problem pictures were more self-contained than illustrations of Cervantes, in another sense they were not, as they were incomplete without the mental activity of the spectator, and they would have been inconceivable if there had not been an underlying assumption that the function of a picture was to illustrate or tell a story.

Problem pictures seem the complete antithesis of the noble art extolled by Reynolds in his *Discourses,* but the Academy had never managed to live up to Reynolds's high-minded ideals. Reynolds himself did not devote his life to history painting but made his living by painting portraits. By the middle of the nineteenth century the exhibitions of the Royal Academy had become popular entertainments. Most modern painting as we know it today traces its history to those artists who opted out of the Academy (or out of the *Salon*) and is seen only by a relatively small and sophisticated public. The audience to which the Royal Academy exhibitions catered was more closely comparable to that cultivated by Hollywood. Indeed, in style, in emotional content, in range of subject matter, and in emphasis upon narrative generally above all else, most pictures exhibited at the Royal Academy have more in common with the movies than with twentieth-century post-Cubist painting. There is not much similarity between any of the pictures in this exhibition and, say, a work by Jackson Pollock, but many could pass for stills from movies in which the action is set in the Victorian or earlier periods. Much Victorian painting owes substantial debts to the theater; Maclise's *Play Scene in Hamlet* (see No. 43), based ultimately upon a production by Charles Kemble, is an obvious example, but many other artists such as Charles Robert Leslie, Edward Matthew Ward, and Augustus Leopold Egg specialized in scenes treated as if they were being acted in period costume upon the stage. In return, many artists contributed designs for Victorian stage sets, and their pictures were to provide a repertory of images upon which twentieth-century moviemakers could draw, consciously or unconsciously.[15] Early movies depended heavily upon the theater, but, since the lights go out when the performance is over, the temporal nature of theatrical productions worked against their potential usefulness as visual sources; the paintings, however, continued to exist after the close of an Academy exhibition, and through the widespread distribution of engravings the creations of Frith or Alma-Tadema had a circulation unrivalled by even the most hard-traveling theatrical company.

The cinema not only owes debts to nineteenth-century academic painting, it also has superseded it. Before the invention of the camera, and particularly the cinematographic camera which was much better at telling stories, painting (and the related arts of drawing and printmaking) fulfilled universally understood functions. The paintings of John Frederick Lewis and Charles Robert Leslie showed the Victorian public what remote places looked like and allowed it to visualize its favorite literary characters. Now we have Louis Malle's *Phantom India* and Marlon Brando in *The Godfather.* The twentieth-century notion that painting should be about painting and not about all the things that fill these Victorian canvases is the outgrowth of the camera's taking over the painter's traditional role as the maker of representational images. Hence, by the principles taught in most Art Appreciation courses, the majority of the pictures in this exhibition may seem all wrong. But to judge them by those principles is to judge them by principles which, to their painters, would have seemed as irrelevant and ridiculous as the theatrical ideas of Bertolt Brecht or the Living Theater would have seemed to a Hollywood producer of the 1930s. Like old movies, these pictures do contain many formal beauties, but they were made to be enjoyed, not to be appreciated by dint of their conformity to some aesthetic canon.

Having said this, we should note that the word "aesthetic," like "philistine," was imported into English by the Victorians. The Aesthetic Movement of the 1870s and 1880s, which is represented in its purest form by Albert Moore's small *Flower Walk* of 1875 (see No. 48), deliberately renounced sentiment, narrative, and the other ingredients that brought success in the Academy exhibitions. Aestheticism was a formalist movement which was never widely popular. It was pilloried in periodicals such as *Punch* and by Gilbert and Sullivan in *Patience,* but Victorian society was rich enough and diverse enough to support Moore as well as Frith. Artists did not have to swim in the mainstream to survive. From William Blake at the beginning of the nineteenth century to the members of the New English Art Club at the end, a steady series of artists either attacked or ignored what they believed the Royal Academy to stand for. During the Victorian period the most vigorous and influential rebellion was that of the Pre-Raphaelite Brotherhood in 1848, and, although Pre-Raphaelitism was formed out of many ingredients, a central one was dislike of the majority of pictures which the slightly older colleagues of Dante Gabriel Rossetti, Holman Hunt, and John Everett Millais were exhibiting annually at the Academy. In 1850 Rossetti dismissed all these pictures as "so closely resembling each other (though from different hands) as hardly to establish a separate recollection."[16] The Pre-Raphaelites broke out of the mold, and they were followed by others. The Aestheticism of Moore and Whistler, and the revived Classicism of Frederic Leighton and Edward Poynter, both of whom had been trained on the Continent, represented significant departures from prevailing patterns in English painting. There was considerable innovation in Victorian art, and although some independent artists, notably Rossetti and Burne-Jones, deliberately turned their backs on the Royal Academy, for others, such as Millais and Hunt, who sent all their early pictures there, the Academy's walls were the site of the battle. For those artists in rebellion against it, as for its most loyal members, the Academy remained the indispensable center of artistic life in England through the Victorian period.

Today the Royal Academy survives intact as an institution, but it no longer holds its central position. It was probably inevitable that an organization founded in the eighteenth century, and grown fat and prosperous in the nineteenth, would not readily adapt itself to the new winds of the twentieth. The Victorian Academy remained Victorian long after the death of the Queen. Its president through the first World War was Edward Poynter, who first sent a picture to the Academy in 1861, and from 1924 to 1928 the president was Frank Dicksee, who also had been exhibiting for over half a century. Poynter probably would have not have been a bad leader twenty years earlier; Frederic Leighton, of whom he often seems an alter-ego, was an admirably open-minded and reforming president of the Academy from 1878 to 1896. But to Roger Fry, who organized the first important exhibitions of contemporary French art in London in 1910 and 1912, Poynter and the institution he led represented the dead hand of another century lying heavy on the present. To a critic trying to explain Cézanne and Matisse to an English public, the authority of Poynter, who was also director of the National Gallery from 1894 to 1906, or the great public popularity of Benjamin Williams Leader, who exhibited steadily until 1923, were outrages which had to be attacked. Much critical comment since Fry has echoed his sentiments; a review published in 1974 of some of the pictures in this exhibition dismissed them as "wrong art."[17] For Fry and his generation the Victorians were a threat, a heritage against which modernists had to struggle to free themselves, but now, three-quarters of the way through the twentieth century, the Victorians no longer threaten. In many ways, they are already so far away, that their civilization, instead of posing burdens upon us, seems almost incomprehensible; their fierce theological controversies, for example, are as remote as those of the Byzantine Empire. A painting such as John Rogers Herbert's *Monastery in the Fourteenth Century* (see No. 24), had a polemical message for his contemporaries which it can never have for us, however much we may admire it as a picture. Since, if we read at all, we no longer read the same books the Victorians read, the subjects of their literary pictures are not readily comprehensible to us; and even if we have read the same books, the passage of a century has taught us to read them in different ways, just as it has taught us to look at works of art in different ways. Perforce, we must see even the most popular Victorian pictures in ways very different than those of the Victorian public. Our eyes are not nineteenth-century eyes, but neither are they the eyes of our grandparents, who had to accept or reject their immediate past. We need not admire all Victorian pictures indiscriminately; no Victorian would have liked all the pictures he saw at a Royal Academy exhibition. But we should be ready to look at them as the art of their time, not as alternatives to the art of our own. They have come into the perspective of history.

ALLEN STALEY

1. It should be said that the selective principle has been at work, and that the quality of the pictures in this exhibition is higher than it would be if this were an absolutely representative sampling of all the works exhibited at the Royal Academy during Victoria's reign, were such a thing possible. A typical Academy exhibition also would have included a higher proportion of landscapes and a much higher proportion of portraits, many of them rather dreary "official" commissions for the clubs and offices where they still hang.

2. Quoted in Sidney C. Hutchison, *The History of the Royal Academy 1768-1968*, London 1968, p. 43. This is the most up-to-date and useful account of the Academy's history. For the Academy in the Victorian era, see also George Dunlop Leslie, R.A., *The Inner Life of the Royal Academy: With an Account of Its Schools and Exhibitions Principally in the Reign of Queen Victoria*, London and New York, 1914.

3. The record was 2,245 works exhibited in 1914 (Hutchison, p. 150). These numbers include not only paintings, but also drawings, prints, sculptures, miniatures, and architectural designs.

4. In 1870 the Academy also began to organize loan exhibitions, usually of Old Masters or recently deceased artists. Although there are now exhibitions at the Academy at all times of the year, the first loan exhibitions were held in January and February and consequently were known as "Winter Exhibitions," while the annual "Exhibition of the Works of Living Artists", which chiefly concerns us here, came to be known as the "Summer Exhibition."

5. The record number of works sent in was 14,253 in 1902 (Hutchison, p. 150).

6. It was apparently the practice to hang large works above the line from the formation of the Academy, but this only became a formal rule in 1842 (Hutchison, p. 108).

7. Most of the exceptions were portraits, and even they tended to get smaller in the middle years of the nineteenth century.

8. The most important probably being the growing significance as purchasers of a middle-class public which did not have houses large enough to accommodate very big pictures.

9. *The Works of John Ruskin*, E. T. Cook and Alexander Wedderburn, eds., London, 1903-12, XIV, pp. 161-2.

10. Hutchison, pp. 144-5, and Georgiana Burne-Jones, *Memorials of Edward Burne-Jones*, London, 1904, II, pp. 150-5, 232-4. Burne-Jones was an Associate from 1885 until 1893; after his resignation he exhibited two drawings at the Academy in 1894, apparently as a gesture of good will.

11. After the French Revolution the functions of the *Académie Royale* were divided among the *Salon*, the *Ecole*, and a largely honorific *Académie* as separate entities. However, all were under the control of the state, and the same artists often were members of the *Académie* and of *Salon* juries and were the teachers at the

Ecole, so the division of responsibilities was more administrative than real. For an extended discussion, see Albert Boime, *The Academy and French Painting in the Nineteenth Century,* London and New York, 1971.

12. The most important was the Slade School in London, founded in 1871; its first master was Edward Poynter, who had been trained in the French academic system. Poynter was succeeded in 1876 by Alphonse Legros (1837-1911), a French artist who although he had lived in England since 1863 never learned to speak English. Another English *atelier* was Hubert von Herkomer's school at Bushey.

13. *The Journal of Eugène Delacroix,* Lucy Norton, trans., Hubert Wellington, ed., London, 1951, pp. 279-81, 286; and Jacques Lethève, "La connaissance des peintres préraphaélites anglais en France (1855-1900)," *Gazette des Beaux-Arts,* LIII, 1959, pp. 315-28. For additional examples of interest by progressive French artists in English Victorian painting, see Linda Nochlin, "Gustave Courbet's *Meeting:* A Portrait of the Artist as a Wandering Jew," *Art Bulletin,* XLIX, 1967, p. 213, n. 45; and Theodore Reff, "Degas's 'Tableau de Genre,' " *Art Bulletin,* LIV, 1972, pp. 332-7.

14. For a brief discussion of the Hon. John Collier (1850-1934), who was the best-known painter of problem pictures, and for several reproductions, see Mary Clive, *The Day of Reckoning,* London, 1964, pp. 55-60.

15. See Bernard Hanson, "D. W. Griffith: Some Sources," *Art Bulletin,* LIV, 1972, pp. 493-515.

16. This remark was made about the works of the Associate members of the Academy. *The Works of Dante Gabriel Rossetti,* William M. Rossetti, ed., London, 1911, pp. 570-1.

17. Douglas Davis, "Back to the Salon," *Newsweek,* Nov. 4, 1974, p. 97.

ACKNOWLEDGEMENTS

To Allen Staley whose introduction is the first major critical examination of the role of the Royal Academy in the development of British painting during Queen Victoria's reign, and whose editing has contributed greatly to the entries which comprise this catalogue.

To Margaret Kelly who not only wrote the first Appendix but, also, whose long hours of research have made it possible to include much of the information contained in this catalogue.

To those at Princeton University without whose encouragement and support this catalogue might never have been written, especially Wen Fong, Thomas Sloan, David Steadman and Peter Bunnell.

To the Director and the Trustees of The Metropolitan Museum and to Anthony Clark and John Walsh whose enthusiasm and support have made it possible for this Collection to be seen for the first time in New York at the Metropolitan. And to Everett Fahy, now Director of the Frick Collection, who, when at the Metropolitan, first championed this project.

To Andrew Patrick of the Fine Art Society for his advice and patience over the phone, at all hours, which has enabled us to acquire many of the pictures in this Collection; and to Rodney Merrington of Thomas Agnew & Sons who also has been instrumental in facilitating the purchase of several paintings. In addition, to the many dealers and other individuals who have helped in various ways in the formation of this collection.

To Christopher Wood, George Landow, David Robertson, Charles Scribner, Mary Bennett, Richard Ormond and other scholars, who have generously shared their knowledge about various pictures and artists with us and whose studies, published and forthcoming, have contributed and will contribute greatly to the appreciation of nineteenth-century art. And to Roy Fisher of Wildenstein & Company who first aroused our interest in the provenances of pictures.

To John Romeo, Production Manager of *Forbes* Magazine, and his assistants who found time to have the color work in this catalogue done; to Ed Wergeles, Art Director of *Forbes* Magazine, whose help with the cover was indispensable; and to Ruth Gruenberg, a Senior Editor of *Forbes* Magazine, who arranged to have the galley proofs read.

To Otto Nelson whose long hours, at all hours and on all days (including one Easter) behind the camera, have made possible most of the photographs which illustrate this catalogue. To his wife, Margaret, for her assistance, and to Allen Rokach who took several special photographs. And to the other photographers whose efforts illustrate several of the pages which follow. And to the collectors, museums and dealers who have granted permission to reproduce works related to pictures in the Collection.

To Messrs. White Bros., printers, and Trentypo, typesetters, whose good services transformed typescript and photographs into a catalogue.

Finally, to my father. Few in his position would have given the backing and enthusiastic support to an enterprise such as this. To him the catalogue is dedicated.

To all, heartfelt thanks.

CHRISTOPHER FORBES

NOTES TO THE CATALOGUE

All pictures, the titles of which are preceded by an asterisk, will be exhibited at The Metropolitan Museum of Art, New York, from March 11 to April 27, 1975 and at additional museums after September 1975. All the pictures included in this catalogue will be exhibited at the Art Museum, Princeton University, from May 10 to September 15, 1975.

All pictures included in this catalogue are the property of the Forbes Magazine Collection. For information about photographs and reproduction permission, write The Curator, Forbes Magazine Collection, 60 Fifth Avenue, New York 10011. Color slides of all the pictures are also available. For information write: Prothmann Associates, Inc., 650 Thomas Avenue, Baldwin, New York 11510.

CATALOGUE

SIR LAWRENCE ALMA-TADEMA, RA
(1836-1912)

was born in Dronryp, Holland on January 8, 1836. He was the youngest son of Pièter Tadema, a notary, and was christened Lourens Alma (after his godfather) Tadema. The artist's middle and last names began to be hyphenated prior to his debut at the Paris *Salon* of 1864. Artists are listed alphabetically in the *Salon* catalogues, and hence the addition of a hyphen brought Alma-Tadema almost to the front of the book. His father died when he was four and his mother was adamantly opposed to his becoming an artist. However, she relented when at the age of fifteen, Alma-Tadema became ill and the doctor, believing him to be consumptive, announced he had only a few years to live. In 1851, he exhibited in a small Dutch gallery a portrait of his sister. He labeled this opus I and continued to assign opus numbers to his pictures for the rest of his life. *Preparations,* opus CCCCVIII, was completed two months before his death. In 1852 he entered the Antwerp Academy where he studied under Baron Gustave Wappers (1803-1874) and Nicaise de Keyser (1813-1887). After leaving the Academy, he became a pupil of Baron Hendrik Leys (1815-1869), considered at the time to be Belgium's greatest living artist. In 1861 Alma-Tadema had his first great success with *The Education of the Children of Clovis,* which was purchased by the King of the Belgians. Two years later he married and on his honeymoon visited Italy for the first time. Prior to this trip, Alma-Tadema had devoted himself to medieval subjects—similar to those of his master, Baron Leys. After viewing the ruins of ancient Rome, however, the artist began to turn to classical scenes. His interest in antiquity aroused, Alma-Tadema also began studying and painting scenes of ancient Egypt although he did not actually visit the land of the Pharaohs for another fifty years.

In 1865 Alma-Tadema moved from Antwerp to Brussels, and then, after the death of his wife four years later, to London. On July 29, 1871 he married Laura Theresa Epps (1852-1909), an artist in her own right whose pictures have sometimes been confused with those of her husband.

Alma-Tadema began exhibiting at the Royal Academy when he arrived in England in 1869 (changing Lourens to Lawrence). Four years later he became a naturalized British citizen and two years after that he was elected an Associate member of the Royal Academy. In 1879 he attained the rank of Academician, and, on the occasion of Queen Victoria's eightieth birthday, two decades later, he was knighted. In 1905 he was decorated with the Order of Merit by Edward VII. He died in 1912 having shown a total of eighty-three pictures at the Royal Academy. A memorial exhibition of his work was held there the following year.

Bibliography

"The Works of Laurence Alma-Tadema, RA," *Art Journal* 1833, pp. 33-37, 65-68.
Wilfrid Meynell, "Laurens Alma-Tadema, RA," in *Some Modern Artists and Their Work,* ed, Wilfrid Meynell, London, 1883, pp. 76-93.
Frederick G. Stephens, *Artists at Home,* New York, 1884.
George M. Ebers, *Lorenz Alma-Tadema,* New York, 1886 (translated by Mary J. Safford).
Helen Zimmern, "L. Alma-Tadema, RA: His Life and Work," *Art Annual: Supplement to the Art Journal,* 1886.
M. H. Spielmann, "Laurence Alma-Tadema, RA: A Sketch," *Magazine of Art,* 1896/1897, pp. 42-50.
Percy Cross Standing, *Sir Lawrence Alma-Tadema, OM, RA,* London, 1905.
Rudolf Dircks, "The Later Works of Sir Lawrence Alma-Tadema, *Art Annual: Supplement to the Art Journal,* 1910.
Mario Amaya, "The Roman World of Alma-Tadema," *Apollo,* December, 1962, pp. 771-778.
Mario Amaya, "The Painter Who Inspired Hollywood," *The Sunday Times Magazine,* London, February 18, 1968.
Jerry E. Patterson, "The Norman Rockwell of the Pagans or The Return of Alma-Tadema: The Candid Cameraman Collects," *Auction,* February, 1971, pp. 40-43.
Christopher Forbes, *Victorians in Togas: Paintings by Sir Lawrence Alma-Tadema from the Collection of Allen Funt, The Metropolitan Museum of Art,* New York, 1973 (exhibition catalogue).

1. * SPRING FESTIVAL

Oil on canvas: 36 x 21 inches
Inscribed, lower left: *L. Alma-Tadema, op. CCVIII*
Original frame

The subject of this painting is derived from the first book of Virgil's *Georgics* and on the base of the frame, which was designed by the artist, are printed the following lines from lib. i, v. 338-350 of John Dryden's translation:

> When Winter's rage abates, When Cheerful Hours
> Awake the Spring, and Spring Awakes the Flowers,
> On Green Turf They Fearless Limbs Display
> And Celebrate the Mighty Mother's Day
> For then the Hills with Pleasing Shades are Growing
> And Sleeps are Sweeter on the Shaken Ground
> With Milder Beams the Sun Securely Shines.
>
> Fat are the Lambs and Luscious are the Wines.
> Let Every Swain adore Her Power Divine,
> And Milk and Honey mix with Wine;

> Let All the Choir of Clowns Attend the Show,
> In Long Procession, Shouting as they Go,
> Invoking Her to Bless their Yearly Stores,
> Inviting Plenty to their Crowded Floors.
>
> Thus in the Spring, and thus in the Summer's Heat
> Before the Sickles Touch the Ripening Wheat.
> On Ceres call: And Let the Labouring Hind
> With Oaken Wreaths his Hollow Temple Bind:
> On Ceres Let Him Call and Ceres Praise,
> With uncouth Dances and with Country Lays.

The picture was well-received by the critics, when exhibited in London in 1880. The writer for the *Art Journal* considered it "One of the most pleasing works L. Alma-Tadema has exhibited for a long time," while his counterpart at the *Magazine of Art* described it as "A brilliant scene of . . . Roman life . . . instinct with all the joyousness and light of Italian April weather." After praising "the air and the sunshine" which seem "to float and quiver with the dance of the flower-crowned men and women," this critic went on to suggest that the feet, "pointed in a manner which is only taught . . . by a course of most penitental exercises," might have been more pleasing "to eyes which appreciate the natural" had their pose not been so contrived.

Two letters (present location unknown) from Alma-Tadema to Anne W. Penfield were quoted in the American Art Association sale catalogue of 1934. In one, discussing *Spring Festival,* Alma-Tadema declared, "I believe this to be one of the best specimens of my work," and in the other, dated December 6, 1910, he expressed the wish that "This work of mine be cheering to your mind and awake in you the hope and charm of spring."

The figure of the dancing youth with tambourine raised aloft reappeared in Alma-Tadema's *Harvest Festival,* op. CCXX, painted in 1880. In

(continued on page 148)

L. Alma-Tadema, *Harvest Festival* op. CCXX.

1. L. Alma-Tadema, *Spring Festival.*
(*see color Plate I, p. 159*)

SOPHIE ANDERSON (née Gengembre)
(1823-c.1898)

was born in Paris in 1823. Her mother was English and her father, Charles Gengembre, was a French architect and art lover whose friends included the great tragic actor, Talma. She studied briefly in the studio of the historical painter, Baron Charles de Steuben (1788-1856), but his departure for Russia in 1848 cut short her education. After the Revolution of 1848, the Gengembre family moved to America, living first in Cincinatti, then near Pittsburgh. Sophie painted portraits and married an American landscape painter named Walter Anderson. The couple moved to England in 1854, and Mrs. Anderson made her debut at the Royal Academy in the following year with a *Virgin and Child.* Most of her subsequent entries were genre scenes.

For reasons of health, the Andersons moved to Capri in the early 1870s. The change of climate was beneficial, and Mrs. Anderson exhibited regularly at the Royal Academy throughout the Seventies and the Eighties. After twenty years in Capri, she moved back to England and settled in Falmouth. She died about 1898 having exhibited a total of twenty-eight works at the Academy.

She also showed her work at the British Institution, the Society of British Artists, and the Grosvenor Gallery. Mrs. Anderson was a minor but successful artist whose work was found in many prominent collections of the period, such as that of Sir John Aird, who also owned Frank Dicksee's *Chivalry* (see No. 10).

Bibliography

E. Clayton, *English Female Artists,* London, 1876, Vol. II, p. 709.
Christopher Wood, *The Dictionary of Victorian Painters,* London, 1971, p. 3.

artists such as Luke Fildes (q.v.), his brother-in-law, Henry Woods (1846-1921; who specialized in Venetian subjects), and Mrs. Anderson. This picture was painted while the artist was living in Capri, and the models, dressed in local costume, clearly are Italian. However, the Italian setting is incidental; it is not indicated by the title of the picture, and the girls behave exactly like little English girls. Mrs. Anderson's best-known work, *No Walk Today* (Collection Sir David Scott), shows a comparable scene of childhood in a domestic English setting.

Provenance

James Pergram (Sale: Christie's London, November 20, 1970, Lot 231).
Thomas Agnew & Sons, London (Agents).

Exhibitions

Royal Academy, 1878, No. 1331.
Women, Salem Fine Arts Center, Winston-Salem, North Carolina and North Carolina Museum of Art, Raleigh, 1972, No. 18 (reproduced in catalogue).
The Art and Mind of Victorian England: Paintings from the Forbes Magazine Collection, University Gallery, University of Minnesota, Minneapolis, 1974, No. 1 (reproduced in catalogue).

References

M. Brawley Hill, "Introduction," *Women,* Salem Fine Arts Center, Winston-Salem, North Carolina, and North Carolina Museum of Art, Raleigh, 1972, p. xi (exhibition catalogue).
Michael A. Findlay, "Forbes Saves the Queen," *Arts Magazine,* February, 1973, p. 30.
Melvin Waldfogel, "Introduction," *The Art and Mind of Victorian England: Paintings from the Forbes Magazine Collection,* University Gallery, University of Minnesota, Minneapolis, 1974, p. 21 (exhibition catalogue).
Douglas Davis, "Back to the Salon," *Newsweek,* November 4, 1974, p. 97, reproduced p. 97.

2. GUESS AGAIN

Oil on canvas: 38-3/4 x 29-1/2 inches
Inscribed, lower right: *S. Anderson*
Original frame

Guess Again attracted no reviews when it appeared at the Royal Academy in 1878. It belongs to a tradition of picturesque Italian genre subjects established by the Swiss painter Léopold Louis Robert (1794-1835) in the years following the Napoleonic wars and imported into England around 1830 by David Wilkie (q.v.), Charles Eastlake (q.v.), and Thomas Uwins, (1782-1857). In the second half of the nineteenth century this tradition was continued by

2. S. Anderson, *Guess Again*.

JOHN BRETT, ARA
(1831-1902)

was considered by John Ruskin to be "one of my keenest minded friends." Born in Surrey in 1831, he entered the Royal Academy Schools in 1854; two years later he made his debut in the Academy's exhibitions with three portraits. In 1858 his *Stonebreaker* brought lavish praise from Ruskin who declared "in some points of precision it goes beyond anything that the Pre-Raphaelites have done yet." Ruskin concluded his review with the challenge, "If he can paint so lovely a distance from the Surrey Downs . . . what would he not make of the chestnut groves of the Val d'Aosta." The following year, after a summer on the Continent, some of it spent with Ruskin, Brett exhibited his *Val d'Aosta*. This confronted Ruskin with a literal result of the approach to landscape advocated by him in *Modern Painters*, and it came as a disappointment. After praising the picture half-heartedly, he concluded that it was "Mirror's work, not Man's." Brett's friendship with Ruskin gradually slackened and in 1864, it ended following a disagreement over a scientific matter.

After 1870, Brett concentrated almost exclusively on seascapes, spending his summers on his yacht, sketching the British coast. In 1880 one of his Academy entries entitled *Britannia's Realm* (Tate Gallery) was purchased for the nation by the Chantrey Bequest. The following year he was elected an Associate of the Royal Academy. He never achieved the rank of full Academician despite the one hundred and fourteen works he eventually exhibited there before his death on January 7, 1902.

Besides being a painter, Brett was also an enthusiastic scientist. He was a Fellow of the Royal Astronomical Society, and the house which he had built for himself at Putney consisted of dwelling rooms, a studio and an astronomical observatory.

After his generous treatment by Ruskin, later criticism seems to have rankled Brett, and, to one writer who placed his work in "the school of minute elaboration," the artist observed "It is a well established practice that if you cannot dig, and to beg you are ashamed, you go into business as an art critic."

Bibliography

J. Brett, "John Brett", *Art Journal*, 1902, p. 87.
H. H. T. [Herbert Hall Turner], *Monthly Notices of the Royal Astronomical Society*, LXII, 1902, pp. 238-241, (obituary).
Frank Maclean, *Henry Moore, RA*, London, 1905, pp. 167-173.
Allen Staley, *The Pre-Raphaelite Landscape*, London, 1973, pp. 124-137.

3. * PEARLY SUMMER

Oil on canvas: 41 x 84 inches
Original Frame

When *Pearly Summer* was exhibited at the Royal Academy in 1893 the following dialogue appeared in the catalogue under the title:

SKIPPER OF SMACK:	"Stand by to cast off!"
MASTER OF TUG:	"Ease her!"
COX OF SHORE BOAT:	"Way enough, mates; she'll just fetch us."

These words seem strangely unrelated to the picture that they accompany. Sailors and ships form but a small fraction of a canvas dominated by vast expanses of sea and sky. Even land is reduced to the faint suggestion of mountains on the right. The action suggested by the commands of the skipper, the tug master and the cox is contradicted by the scale of the ships and by the lazy feeling of summer tranquility which pervades the painting.

The critic reviewing the Academy exhibition for the *Magazine of Art* observed:

> In *Pearly Summer* Mr. Brett returns to the triumphs of his *Britannia's Realm*, the chiefest merit lying not in the breadth of his highly worked-up sea, but in the extraordinary amount of light with which he has filled the picture.

Pearly Summer is similar to *Britannia's Realm* (Tate Gallery), but the ships are less remote than those in the earlier work, and the space depicted is less vast. Unlike most of Brett's pictures, neither purports to show an identifiable location, but whereas the title of *Britannia's Realm* suggests that the painting symbolizes Britain's authority over the seas, the title *Pearly Summer* indicates that the prime concern in this painting is the effect of light. In several essays published during the latter years of his life, Brett emphasized the essential importance of a quasi-scientific knowledge of light and other natural effects for the landscape and seascape painter. This knowledge is evident in the changing light of the sky and its reflections in the water in *Pearly Summer*. Brett was a professed admirer of Turner, whom he proclaimed the greatest of all modern artists, and the broadly painted clouds in *Pearly Summer* recall those in pictures by Turner such as the *Entrance of the Meuse* (Tate Gallery), exhibited at the Royal Academy in 1819. The interest in nautical activities manifested by the lines printed in the Royal Academy catalogue also recalls similar interests of Turner, which are evident in such works as the *Entrance of the Meuse* and "*Now for the painter*" (RA, 1827; City Art Gallery, Manchester).

Pearly Summer remained in the artist's possession until his death. It was one of the English pictures selected to be sent to Paris for the *Exposition Universelle* of 1900, where it won a Silver Medal.

Provenance

Artist's Sale: Christie's, London, February 15, 1909, Lot 120, 105 gns.
Anon. Sale: Christie's, London, March 5, 1971, Lot 62.
Fine Art Society, London (Agents).

Exhibitions

Royal Academy, 1893, No. 153.
Exposition Universelle, Paris, 1900, No. 25 (Silver Medal).
The Art and Mind of Victorian England: Paintings from the Forbes Magazine Collection, University Gallery, University of Minnesota, Minneapolis, September 28-November 8, 1974, No. 3 (reproduced in catalogue).

References

Henry Blackburn, *Academy Notes*, London, 1893, p. 10, reproduced p. 56.
The Illustrated London News, May 6, 1893, p. 547.
Magazine of Art, vol. XVI, 1893, p. 256.
Royal Academy Pictures: Supplement of The Magazine of Art, 1893, reproduced p. 100.
Magazine of Art, vol. XXV, 1901, reproduced p. 219 (View of northside of Room XXVII, *Exposition Universelle*; see upper left corner).
Melvin Waldfogel, "Introduction," *The Art and Mind of Victorian England: Paintings from the Forbes Magazine Collection*, University Gallery, University of Minnesota, Minneapolis, 1974, p. 22 (exhibition catalogue).

Forthcoming References

George Landow, "There began to be a great talking about the Fine Arts," University of Minnesota Lecture Series, October 17, 1974 (to be published in 1975).

J. Brett, *Britannia's Realm* (The Tate Gallery, London)

3. J. Brett, *Pearly Summer.*
(*see color Plate XXIII, p. 181*)

JOHN BURR

(1834-1893)

was born in Edinburgh in 1834. Both he and his younger brother, Alexander Hohenlohe Burr (1835-1899), became practicing artists. At the age of fourteen the older Burr began painting portraits of local notables in small Scottish towns. Five years later he entered the Trustee's Academy in Edinburgh where he studied under Robert Scott Lauder (1803-1869). While a student he began exhibiting at the Royal Scottish Academy, and his contributions of 1857 and 1858 were purchased by the Association for the Promotion of the Fine Arts in Scotland. In the year 1861 both Burr brothers moved to London. They began exhibiting at the Royal Academy the next year.

Almost all of the eighteen works that the elder Burr exhibited at the Academy were precise, often humorous genre scenes reminiscent of the work of his compatriot Thomas Faed (1826-1900) but lacking somewhat in the latter's sympathy for his subjects. As one critic put it, the characters depicted by Burr "are always characters." Nevertheless, he made a reputation for himself, and was an Associate of the Old Watercolour Society and President of the Society of British Artists, preceding Whistler in that post. He stopped exhibiting at the Royal Academy in 1882 and died in 1893, spending the last years of his life in relative obscurity.

Bibliography

James Dafforne, "John Burr," *Art Journal,* 1869, pp. 337-339.
James L. Caw, *Scottish Painting, Past and Present 1620-1908,* Edinburgh, 1908, p. 262.
S. Cursiter, *Scottish Art,* New York, 1949, pp. 101, 123.

4. THE PEEPSHOW

Oil on canvas: 30 x 25 inches
Inscribed, lower right: *J. Burr*
Original frame

The Peepshow is typical of Burr's *oeuvre.* It is precisely painted, and the subject is one with which the viewer identifies easily. The picture was exhibited at the Royal Academy in the same year as Thomas Webster's (q.v.) *Battle of Waterloo.* This more complex and more amusing composition also depicted a penny peepshow and it received a glowing review in the *Art Journal,* while Burr's work of a similar subject was not mentioned. Five years later, however, James Dafforne, writing in the same magazine described the subject in enthusiastic terms and

concluded: *"The Peepshow . . .* is a humorous and very clever composition of its kind, presented in a manner that would bring credit to any artist, even of high reputation."

Such unpretentious scenes of childhood have never lost their popular appeal; the *Saturday Evening Post* covers of Norman Rockwell are their twentieth-century descendants. One hundred and six years after it appeared on the walls of the Royal Academy, *The Peepshow* itself appeared on the cover of the Christmas Number of *The Illustrated London News.*

Provenance

Anon. Sale: Christie's, Hopetoun House, Lothian, October 15, 1969, Lot 117.
Fine Art Society, London.

Exhibitions

Royal Academy, 1864, No. 523.
100 Years of Scottish Painting, English Speaking Union Gallery (presented by the Fine Art Society), Edinburgh, 1970, No. 11.
The Art and Mind of Victorian England: Paintings from the Forbes Magazine Collection, University Gallery, University of Minnesota, Minneapolis, 1974, No. 4 (reproduced in catalogue).

References

James Dafforne, "John Burr," *Art Journal,* 1869, p. 337.
The Illustrated London News, Christmas Number, 1970, reproduced on front cover in color, reproduced p. i.
Christopher Wood, *The Dictionary of Victorian Painters,* London, 1971, p. 19, reproduced p. 226.
"Forbes Gift Subscriptions," *Forbes,* November 1, 1972, p. 78, November 15, 1972, p. 103, December 1, 1972, p. 64, reproduced in color in each (advertisement).
Melvin Waldfogel, "Introduction," *The Art and Mind of Victorian England: Paintings from the Forbes Magazine Collection,* University Gallery, University of Minnesota, Minneapolis, 1974, p. 21 (exhibition catalogue).

4. J. Burr, *The Peepshow*.

PHILIP HERMOGENES CALDERON, RA
(1833-1898)

was born in Poitiers in 1833, the son of an un-
conventional Spanish Priest and his French wife.
From his father, who became Professor of
Spanish literature at King's College, London,
Calderon received his education. At the age of
seventeen, he entered J. M. Leigh's art school
in Newman Street. The following year he went
to Paris where with his friend and future fellow
member of the St. John's Wood Clique (see
Appendix I), Henry Stacy Marks (1829-1898),
he was accepted as a student in the *atelier*
of the *Salon* painter, François Edouard Picot
(1786-1868). In 1853, he made his debut at the
Royal Academy with an Old Testament work
entitled, *"By the Waters of Babylon, there we sat
down. Yea we wept when we remembered Zion."*
During the next forty-four years Calderon exhibited an additional one hundred and four
works, principally historical, biblical or imaginative period genre scenes at the Academy's
annual summer shows. The influence of his
training in France is apparent in most of these.

Calderon was elected an Associate member in
1864 and a full Royal Academician in 1867. That
same year his *Her Most High, Noble and Puis-
sant Grace* was the only British picture to receive
a Gold Medal at the *Exposition Universelle* in
Paris. In 1887, he was appointed Keeper of the
Royal Academy. He died in London twelve years
later.

Bibliography
W. W. Fenn, "Our Living Artists, Philip Hermogenes
Calderon, RA," *Magazine of Art*, Vol. I, 1878, p. 200.
Clara Clement and Lawrence Hutton, *Artists of the
Nineteenth Century*, London, 1879, pp. 115-116.
W. W. Fenn, "P. H. Calderon, RA," in *Some Modern
Artists and Their Work*, ed. Wilfrid Meynell, London,
1883, pp. 234-239.
Frederick G. Stephens, *Artists at Home*, New York,
1884.
Philip Hermogenes Calderon, "Catalogue" (unpub-
lished manuscript illustrated with sketches, Collection
of Jeremy Mass, London).
Bevis Hillier, "The St. John's Wood Clique," *Apollo*,
June, 1964, pp. 490-495.

5. * THE MOONLIGHT SERENADE
Oil on canvas: 16-3/4 x 34-3/4 inches
Inscribed, lower right: *P. H. Calderon, — 1872*
and verso, lower right: *Philip H. Calderon,.
9 Marlboro Place, St. John's Wood.*
Original frame

The Moonlight Serenade, or *The Interrupted
Serenade* as it has sometimes been called,
was described by Calderon in his handwritten
catalogue as follows:

> Painted with Roberson's medium — long,
> narrow picture — on the right a window with
> railings, candle light inside, and a fright-
> ened woman eagerly looking out — under
> window a smashed mandoline — in the centre
> — infuriated husband or brother, sword in
> hand, running at full speed after the musical
> but cowardly lover, who is clean around the
> corner, on the left, flying for his life — down a
> moonlit street.

When *The Moonlight Serenade* appeared at the
Royal Academy in 1873, it attracted only slight
critical attention. In the *Art Journal,* the reviewer concluded "the incidents are so well set
forth that every point is intelligible." *Punch*
suggested much the same thing in its "Academy
Rhymes":

> As for his *Victory* and *Serenade* —
>   In neither is the point of the subject
>   miss'd:
> The story's clear, characters well portrayed.
>   What's CALDERON, if not a dramatist?

The picture is highly theatrical; the broken
mandolin, the lost shoe, and the candlelit window were all stock props of romantic farces of
this genre. Calderon's training in the *atelier* of
Picot is evident in the French feeling of the picture. The technique and figural scale are
reminiscent of Jean-Léon Gérôme (1824-
1904), and the theatricality of the subject also
recalls works by Gérôme such as the well-
known *Duel after the Ball* of 1857 (Musée
Condé, Chantilly), but on a comic rather than
tragic level. Gérôme took up temporary residence in London in 1870 during the siege of
Paris. He exhibited at the Royal Academy in
1870 and 1871, and was elected an Honorary
Member of the Royal Academy shortly before
Calderon painted *The Moonlight Serenade.*

Provenance
Anon. Sale: Christie's, London, October 22, 1971,
Lot 62.
Fine Art Society, London (Agents).

Exhibitions
Royal Academy, 1873, No. 181.
*The Art and Mind of Victorian England: Paintings from
the Forbes Magazine Collection,* University Gallery,
University of Minnesota, Minneapolis, 1974, No. 5
(reproduced in catalogue).

References
Art Journal, 1873, p. 168.
"Academy Rhymes," *Punch*, May 17, 1873, p. 206.
W. W. Fenn, "Our Living Artists, Philip Hermogenes
Calderon, RA," *Magazine of Art*, Vol. I, 1878,
p. 200.
Clara Clement and Lawrence Hutton, *Artists of the
Nineteenth Century*, London, 1879, p. 115.
Frederick G. Stephens, *Artists at Home,* New York,
1884, p. 67.
Philip Hermogenes Calderon, "Catalogue", p. 37,
reproduced p. 36 (unpublished manuscript
illustrated with sketches, Collection of Jeremy
Mass, London).

5. P. H. Calderon, *The Moonlight Serenade.*

JAMES COLLINSON
(c. 1825-1887)

one of the seven original members of the Pre-Raphaelite Brotherhood (see Appendix I), was born around 1825 the son of a bookseller in Mansfield, Nottinghamshire. He studied at the Royal Academy Schools and in 1847 exhibited at the Royal Academy for the first time. The picture, entitled *The Charity Boy's Debut*, was Collinson's first major work, and it received good reviews. Furthermore, it prompted Dante Gabriel Rossetti to pronounce Collinson "a born stunner," and sponsor his membership in the PRB. Collinson had converted to Catholicism, but returned to the Anglican Church in order to persuade Christina Rosetti (the sister of Dante Gabriel and William Michael Rossetti) to accept his proposal of marriage. However, in 1850, after an engagement of nearly two years, he reaffirmed his faith in the Catholic Church, and she broke off the engagement. Collinson later married a sister-in-law of another Catholic convert, the painter John Rogers Herbert (q.v.). In 1850 he resigned from the PRB and entered a Jesuit monastery, but he remained there only three or four years.

His only major Pre-Raphaelite work, *The Renunciation of Queen Elizabeth of Hungary*, depicts an episode described in Charles Kingsley's *The Saint's Tragedy*. Completed in November 1850, the picture was exhibited at the Portland Gallery the following year. The remainder of Collinson's known works are almost exclusively of contemporary genre subjects. Between 1847 and 1870 he exhibited seventeen paintings at the Royal Academy, and he also contributed to the exhibitions of the Society of British Artists and the British Institution. Although he did not die until January 4, 1881, he seems to have ceased painting after about 1870. He died in almost complete obscurity.

Bibliography

Thomas Bodkin, "James Collinson," *Apollo*, May, 1940, pp. 128-133.
Christopher Wood, *The Dictionary of Victorian Painters*, London, 1971, p. 29.

6. * TO LET

Oil on canvas: oval — 23 x 18 inches

The subject is a married lady who is pulling up a Venetian blind which reveals a sign in the window offering furnished apartments. Unlike most contemporary genre subjects of this period, the relationship of the title to the contents of the painting is not immediately obvious. The critic of the *Art Journal*, while admitting

that the figure "is round and well drawn," complained that the "point of the title is not very clear." Even when one finally becomes aware of what is written on the sign in the window, the painting remains open to diverse interpretations. Some eighty years after the painting first appeared at the Royal Academy, when it was lent to an exhibition at the Leicester Galleries with its pendant, a similar oval composition entitled *For Sale* (Nottingham Museum), the critic of the *Times* observed: "There are hints . . . in the pair of pictures *For Sale* and *To Let* by James Collinson . . . that some Victorian artists had pretty shrewd notions about comparative iniquity." Although the women in both pictures apparently seemed excessively inviting to the *Times's* critic, there is no reason to believe that Collinson intended any such *double-entendre*.

To Let and *For Sale* seem to have been Collinson's most popular works. A pair of replicas is in the Graves Art Gallery in Sheffield. Almost identical in every detail to their predecessors, these two pictures are less suggestively entitled *The Landlady* and *The Bazaar*. Another replica of *For Sale*, entitled *The Empty Purse* is now in the Tate Gallery.

The inspiration for these paintings may have been William Powell Frith's successful oval composition of a few years earlier entitled "*Sherry, Sir?*". *To Let* was engraved in 1858 as a pendant to a third composition by Collinson, engraved a year earlier and now lost, entitled *Good for a Cold*. This picture also had an oval format dominated by a single female figure. In the engraving *To Let* is subtitled "*A Fine Prospect, Sir.*" *To Let* and *Good for a Cold* appear to have been the only works by Collinson to have been engraved.

Provenance

Professor Thomas Bodkin (Sale: Sotheby's, London, November 11, 1959, Lot 98, reproduced).
Fine Art Society, London.

Exhibitions

Royal Academy, 1857, No. 102.
Birmingham City Museum and Art Gallery, 1919.
Municipal Gallery of Modern Art, Dublin, 1920.
Victorian Exhibition, Birmingham City Museum and Art Gallery, 1937, No. 98.
Exhibition of Victorian Life, Leicester Galleries, London, 1937, No. 98.
The Pre-Raphaelite Brotherhood, Birmingham City Museum and Art Gallery, 1947, No. 17.
Pre-Raphaelite Exhibition, Lady Lever Art Gallery, Port Sunlight, 1948, No. 99.
Exhibition of Paintings and Drawings by the Pre-Raphaelites and Their Followers, Russell-Cotes Art Gallery, Bournemouth, June-August, 1951, No. 24.
Some Pre-Raphaelite Paintings and Drawings, Arts Council, Wales, 1955, No. 21.
Victorian Painting, Nottingham University Art Gallery, 1959, No. 12.
Victorian Paintings, Charles Keyser Gallery, London, 1971.
Victorian Art, The Emily Lowe Gallery, Hofstra University, Hempstead, New York, 1972, No. 66 (reproduced in catalogue).
On loan to The Metropolitan Museum of Art, New York, August, 1974-March, 1975, Loan No. L. 1974.62.

References

Art Journal, 1857, p. 167.
Thomas Bodkin, "James Collinson," *Apollo*, May, 1940, pp. 130, 132-133, reproduced p. 130, fig. III.
William E. Fredeman, *Pre-Raphaelitism: A Biblio-critical Study*, Cambridge, Massachusetts, 1965, p. 132.
Victorian Paintings, Mappin Art Gallery, Sheffield, 1968, p. 17, No. 35, 1 (exhibition catalogue).
Michael A. Findlay, "Forbes Saves the Queen," *Arts Magazine*, February, 1973, reproduced p. 29.

J. Collinson, *For Sale*
(Nottingham Museum)

J. Collinson, *Good for a Cold*

6. J. Collinson, *To Let.*
(*see color Plate II, p. 160*)

THOMAS SIDNEY COOPER, RA

(1803-1902)

was one of the most long-lived artists in history. Between 1833 and 1902 he exhibited some two hundred and sixty-six works at the Royal Academy without missing a year, a record for continuity that has never been equalled.

Cooper was born in Canterbury on September 26, 1803. When he was five, he and his four brothers and sisters were abandoned by their father. He received very little formal education and earned his first shilling as an artist when a man paid him not to draw on Sundays. Because of his family's poverty, Cooper's earliest graphic efforts were confined to a slate, until George Cattermole (1800-1868), the watercolor painter, impressed by one of his efforts, provided him with a large quantity of paper and a dozen pencils. Having no knife to keep them sharpened, Cooper prevailed upon passersby to cut the points. Among the passersby was the Archbishop of Canterbury who also gave Cooper £5 for one of his renderings of Canterbury Cathedral.

Cooper first learned perspective from a Mr. Doyle at the local theater and was eventually hired to replace him. In 1825 Cooper went to London to stay with a maternal uncle, and after his arrival he began studying at the British Museum. Unfortunately, just after he was accepted as a student in the Royal Academy Schools, he had to return to Canterbury, where he became a drawing master. In 1827 he set out for the Continent with a friend, and ended up staying in Brussels and becoming a teacher. While in Brussels he was influenced by the Belgian animal painter, Eugene Verboeckhoven (1798(9?)-1881), and by the works of the seventeenth-century Dutch masters such as Paulus Potter (1625-1654). In 1831 he returned to England and settled in London, and in 1833 he made his debut at the Royal Academy's annual exhibition with *Landscape and Cattle*. He was consistent in his choice of subjects. One of his last works exhibited at the Royal Academy in 1902, just after his death in February of that year, was entitled *Harbledown, Near Canterbury: Trees, 1848; Cattle and Landscape, 1901.* He was elected an Associate of the Royal Academy in 1845 and a full Member in 1867. Between 1847 and 1856 he painted many works in collaboration with Frederick Richard Lee (q.v.), one of which is in this exhibition (see No. 36).

Cooper described his *oeuvre* in his memoirs published in 1890 as follows:

> Although a great many of them were more or less cattle pieces, and most of them quiet rural scenes, I endeavored to introduce some variety into the treatment of the different subjects, and I must admit that they found favour generally, and I was fortunate in selling nearly all of them which must be accepted as proof of my success.

Bibliography

Thomas Sidney Cooper, "Memoir of T. S. Cooper, ARA," *Art Journal*, 1849, pp. 336-337.
James Dafforne, "British Artists: Their Style and Character; No. LV—Thomas Sidney Cooper, ARA," *Art Journal*, 1861, pp. 133-135.
Art Journal, 1902, p. 125, (obituary).
Thomas Sidney Cooper, *My Life*, 2 Vols., London, 1890.

7. REPOSING ON GOD'S ACRE

Oil on canvas: 48 x 64-1/4 inches
Inscribed, lower right: *T. Sidney Cooper R.A. 1875*

Reposing on God's Acre was one of three works exhibited by Cooper at the Royal Academy in 1875. They received almost no notice from the press. In his memoirs, however, Cooper noted: "To the Exhibition of 1875 I sent three paintings, of which *Reposing on God's Acre*, a scene in a churchyard with sheep, seemed to be the most generally noticed."

The painting shows Cooper's characteristic virtuosity in the rendering of the texture of the sheep's wool. The space is more compressed than in most of Cooper's pictures, but in most of his pictures sheep or cattle are seen in open fields, not in the confined space of a churchyard. "God's Acre" is a traditional English term for a burial ground. Sheep, since early Christian times, have traditionally been associated with the church, as the pastoral flock tended by the Good Shepherd, and they bear this symbolic meaning in many Victorian pictures, such as Holman Hunt's *Hireling Shepherd* (RA, 1852; City Art Gallery, Manchester). Whether Cooper intended explicit symbolism in *Reposing on God's Acre* is open to question, but for Victorian viewers some religious associations would have been inescapable. Cooper may have been inspired to paint this picture by Sir Edwin Landseer's painting exhibited at the Royal Academy three years earlier, *The Baptismal Font* (Royal Collection), which shows a flock of sheep gathered around a font carved with a head of the Man of Sorrows. As Landseer died in 1873, it is even possible that Cooper intended this graveyard scene as a personal epitaph for his fellow animal painter. The tools in the foreground indicate that a grave either has just been or is about to be dug.

God's Acre, Evening, painted in 1894 by Benjamin Williams Leader (q.v.), depicts the same graveyard viewed from a greater distance.

Provenance

Anon. Sale: Phillips, London, June 22, 1970, Lot P.139.

Exhibitions

Royal Academy, 1875, No. 246.

References

Henry Blackburn, *Academy Notes*, London, 1875, p. 24.
The Illustrated London News, May 22, 1875, p. 486.
Clara Clement and Lawrence Hutton, *Artists of the Nineteenth Century*, London, 1879, p. 154.
Thomas Sidney Cooper, *My Life*, London, 1890, Vol. II, pp. ix, 190, 319.
Muriel Freeman, "Kinetic Art in the Forbes Collection," *New Jersey Music & Arts*, November, 1974, reproduced p. 35 (gallery view, see upper center).

B. W. Leader, *God's Acre, Evening*
(Photograph: Sotheby's Belgravia)

7. T. S. Cooper, *Reposing on God's Acre.*

ERNEST CROFTS, RA
(1847-1911)

was born in Leeds on September 15, 1847. He became the pupil of a short-lived painter named Alfred Barron Clay (1831-1868), from whom he acquired a taste for history painting. Two years after Clay's death, Crofts moved to Düsseldorf where he studied under Emil Hünten (1827-1902). Hünten had accompanied the Prussian army during the annexation of Schleswig-Holstein in 1864 and thereafter devoted himself principally to battle painting. This preference he instilled in his English pupil, whose first picture exhibited at the Royal Academy in 1874 was entitled *A Retreat: Episode in the German-French War*. Crofts remained in Germany until the late 1870s, when he returned to England, eventually settling in St. John's Wood. His *On the Morning of the Battle of Waterloo* of 1876 and *Wellington's March from Quatre Bras to Waterloo* of 1878 were well received, the former being included at the *Exposition Universelle* in Paris in 1878. At the *Exposition* of eleven years later he won a Bronze Medal. Crofts's continued success with military subjects established him with Laslett John Pott (q.v.) and Lady Elisabeth Butler (née Thompson; 1846-1933) as the pre-eminent Victorian practitioners of that genre. Crofts also made a reputation for himself as an illustrator.

He was elected an Associate Academician in 1878 and a full Academician along with George Henry Boughton (1833-1905) in 1896. Two years later he succeeded Philip Hermogenes Calderon (q.v.) as Keeper of the Royal Academy. Before his death in London on March 20, 1911, Crofts exhibited forty-seven works at the Academy.

Bibliography
Christopher Wood, *The Dictionary of Victorian Painters*, London, 1971, p. 33.

8. * WHITEHALL: JANUARY 30th, 1649

Oil on canvas: 66-1/2 x 51 inches
Inscribed, lower right: *E. Crofts 1890*

Although Crofts's title is deliberately cryptic, any Victorian at all conversant with the history of his country would have recognized the subject of the picture as the execution of Charles I (1600-1649). The King is seen on a scaffold erected before Inigo Jones's Banqueting House in Whitehall. He is accompanied by William Juxon (1582-1663), the Bishop of London, whom Charles had selected to be with him to administer the last consolations of religion. According to historical accounts, Roundhead troops surrounded the scaffold to keep the citizens away. Charles's dignity and graciousness in his final hours are also recorded. His last word to Juxon was "Remember".

Whitehall: January 30th, 1649 was the subject of extensive reviews when it was exhibited at the Royal Academy in 1890. It was chosen by the *Magazine of Art* as the frontispiece to the second part of its *Academy Pictures*, and it received a full page illustration in Blackburn's *Academy Notes*. The critic for the *Art Journal* thought it particularly commendable that the Royal Martyr, his attendants and his executioners were not the center of attention. "Very curious, but by no means regrettable, is the comparative absence of those pseudo-romantic subjects from history and romance which delight the heart of the *bourgeois* in general, and the visitor to the Royal Academy in particular." M. H. Spielmann, writing for the *Magazine of Art*, was more reserved in his judgment: "Mr. Crofts . . . has realized with considerable power the execution scene of Charles I. It is a highly dramatic composition, but it suffers from the absence of atmosphere." *Punch* parodied the picture with a cartoon, and the reviewer for *The Illustrated London News*, while acknowledging that *Whitehall* was one of the principal historical pictures of the year, went on to carp that the event was depicted "otherwise than in accordance with the best accepted version."

Whitehall, January 30th, 1649 was Crofts's second portrayal of the last moments of the unfortunate King. In 1883, he exhibited *Charles I on His Way to Execution* at the Royal Academy. In this picture, too, he passed over the obvious dramatic moment of the raising of the axe. Instead the King was depicted walking through St. James's Park accompanied by Juxon en route to Whitehall.

Provenance
Marcus van Raalte
Mrs. Charles van Raalte
Anon. Sale: Sotheby's Belgravia, October 19, 1971, Lot 109.
Thomas Agnew & Sons, London

Exhibitions
Royal Academy, 1890, No. 216.
Exposition Universelle, Paris, 1900, No. 60.
Franco-British Exhibition, London, 1908, No. 342.

References
Art Journal, 1890, p. 169.
Henry Blackburn, *Academy Notes*, London, 1890, p. 216, reproduced p. 49.
Magazine of Art, Vol. XIII, 1890, p. 254.
The Illustrated London News, May 10, 1890, p. 594.
"The Pick of the Pictures—Royal Academy," *Punch*, May 24, 1890, p. 250, reproduced.
Royal Academy Pictures: Supplement of the Magazine of Art, 1890, reproduced p. 42.
"Notes and Queries," *Magazine of Art*, Vol. XX, 1897, p. 225.
Sir Isidore Spielmann, *Souvenir of the Fine Art Section: Franco-British Exhibition*, London, 1908, p. 41, reproduced facing p. 153.

No. 216. "Walk up! Walk up! Just a goin' to begin'!"

Punch, 1890

8. E. Crofts, *Whitehall: January 30th, 1649.*

EYRE CROWE, ARA
(1824-1910)

was born on Sloane Street, Chelsea in October, 1824, the son of the historian and author Eyre Crowe, and older brother of J. A. Crowe, who with G. B. Cavalcaselle wrote the *History of Painting in North Italy*. He first studied drawing and painting under William H. Darley (exhibited 1836 to 1850) and then in Paris under Paul Delaroche (1797-1856). In 1844 he was among the pupils selected by Delaroche to accompany him on a trip through Italy. Upon his return to England, Crowe entered the Royal Academy Schools. Two years later he made his debut at the Academy with a historical subject entitled *Master Prynne Searching the Pockets of Archbishop Laud in the Tower, May 31, 1634*. In 1852, Crowe accompanied his cousin, William Makepeace Thackeray, as secretary on an extensive tour through the United States. Two of Crowe's best-known pictures were derived from observations made on this trip: *Slaves Going South After Being Sold — Richmond, Virginia*, exhibited at the Suffolk Street Gallery in 1854, and *Slaves Waiting for Sale — Richmond, Virginia*, exhibited at the Royal Academy in 1861. The outbreak of the Civil War in the United States no doubt prompted Crowe's later return to his American sketches, and emotions of the hour, rather than aesthetics, may well have inspired the critic of the *Art Journal* to describe this picture as "certainly the most promising work of the season. . . ."

Crowe, however, did not live up to his early promise. He became an Associate Academician in 1876, but never rose to the rank of Academician. During his lifetime (he died on December 12, 1910), Crowe exhibited some one hundred and nineteen works at the Royal Academy. The majority of these were historical, literary, or genre subjects.

Bibliography

James Dafforne, "British Artists: Their Style and Character; No. LXXIII — Eyre Crowe," *Art Journal*, 1864, pp. 205-207.
Christopher Wood, *The Dictionary of Victorian Painters*, London, 1971, p. 34.

9. LADY COVENTRY'S ESCORT

First Sketch, oil on canvas:
12-3/4 x 16-1/2 inches
Second Sketch, oil on canvas:
12-1/4 x 18-1/4 inches
Third Sketch, oil on canvas:
12-1/4 x 18-1/4 inches

Lady Coventry's Escort, the picture for which these three sketches are studies, was first exhibited at the Royal Academy in 1892. Other than being reproduced in *The Illustrated London News*, the picture attracted little attention when it appeared at the Academy.

The subject is typical of Crowe — in this case, an unimportant but amusing incident from the reign of King George II. The following quotation from Horace Walpole's *Letters* was included with the entry in the Academy catalogue:

> Lady Coventry having been insulted in the park Sunday se'night, The King heard of it; and he said that to prevent the same for the future, she would have a guard. Upon this foundation her Ladyship ventured boldly again into the park. The whole guard was ready to turn out if there had been occasion.

Lady Maria Coventry (1733-1760) and her younger sister, Elizabeth, were great beauties of their day. Horace Walpole proclaimed her "one of the handsomest women alive." She was a special favorite of George II, and after she had been mobbed by crowds in Hyde Park who were out to see her fabled face, the King ordered that she should have an escort of two servants of the guard and twelve soldiers. Her Ladyship then proceeded to make a fool of herself by flaunting this entourage that next Sunday on an extended walk through the park.

According to the numbers inscribed on the backs of the studies, the finished painting is compositionally closest to Sketch No. 2.

Provenance

First Sketch: Anon. Sale: Sotheby's Belgravia, London, October 24, 1972, Lot 76.
Second Sketch: Anon. Sale: Sotheby's Belgravia, London, October 24, 1972, Lot 77.
Third Sketch: Anon. Sale: Phillip's, London, February 12, 1973, Lot P41.
Anon. Sale: Christie's, London, November 9, 1973, Lot 198.
Fine Art Society, London (Agents).

Exhibitions

The Art and Mind of Victorian England: Paintings from the Forbes Magazine Collection, University Gallery, University of Minnesota, Minneapolis, 1974, No. 7a, b, and c. (all reproduced in catalogue, *First* and *Third Sketch*, 7a and c, were not hung).

E. Crowe, *Lady Coventry's Escort*

9a. E. Crowe, *Lady Coventry's Escort* (first sketch).

9b. E. Crowe, *Lady Coventry's Escort* (second sketch).

9c. E. Crowe, *Lady Coventry's Escort* (third sketch).

SIR FRANK DICKSEE, PRA
(1853-1928)

was born in London on November 27, 1853, into the household of Thomas Dicksee, a self-trained, modestly successful artist who exhibited at the Royal Academy from 1841 to 1895. Christened Francis Bernard Dicksee, the younger Dicksee dropped these given names for his nickname before he began exhibiting in his early 20s. After working with his father for a year and as a probationer for another, he became a full student at the Royal Academy Schools in 1871. There he was impressed and influenced by both Frederic Leighton (q.v.) and John Everett Millais (q.v.). A year after he entered the schools, he won a Silver Medal for drawing from the antique, and during the next few years he produced a number of illustrations for various magazines, including *Cornhill*, *Cassell's* and the *Graphic*. In 1876, he exhibited his first work at the Royal Academy. The painting, a subject from the Old Testament, *Elijah Confronting Ahab and Jezebel in Naboth's Vine Yard,* won a Gold Medal. His entry of 1877, a medieval costume piece entitled *Harmony* (Tate Gallery), was purchased by the Chantrey Bequest for £376 10s. Dicksee continued to paint popular, rich-hued, lavishly costumed pictures of quasi-historical, mythological, biblical and literary subjects throughout the rest of his long and prosperous career. *The Confession* won a Silver Medal at the *Exposition Universelle* of 1900 in Paris, and, in the same year, *The Two Crowns* (Tate Gallery) was voted by a poll of readers of the *Daily News* as the best picture in the Royal Academy exhibition. It was purchased by the Chantrey Bequest for £2000.

Increasingly, beginning in the 1890s Dicksee turned his hand to the lucrative field of portraiture. Elected an Associate member of the Academy in January of 1881 and a Member in 1891, Dicksee was elected President in 1924. He was knighted shortly thereafter. He died four years later on October 17, 1928, and was briefly and accurately described in his obituary in *The Illustrated London News* as "a painter of very popular 'sentimental' works." During his lifetime, Dicksee exhibited one hundred and fifty-three pictures at the Royal Academy.

Bibliography

Sydney Hodges, "Mr. Frank Dicksee, ARA," *Magazine of Art.* Vol. X, 1887, pp. 216-222.
E. Rimboult Dibdin, "Frank Dicksee, RA," *Art Annual: Supplement to the Art Journal*, 1905.

10. * CHIVALRY

Oil on canvas: 72 x 53-1/2 inches
Original frame

Chivalry was commissioned by Sir John Aird and was Dicksee's only work in the Royal Academy exhibition of 1885. The medieval virtue is personified by a clean-shaven knight in shining armour rescuing a fair damsel from a sinister blackguard in dark, dull armour. The initial reviews of the painting were enthusiastic. The critic for the *Art Journal* described *Chivalry* as: "A bold and successful attempt to acclimatize Venetian colouring and medieval mysticism which the Pre-Raphaelites failed to revive." Two years later, Sydney Hodges describing the picture in the *Magazine of Art* praised the,

> return to rich harmonious colouring of the artist's earlier work. The effect of the knight in complete armour, in strong relief against the warm glow of the evening sky was very striking, and the whole picture seemed instinct with the feeling of the Venetians.

In 1905, however, E. Rimbault Dibdin, in his article on Dicksee, observed: "It must be confessed that this ambitious composition is unconvincing, the more so as it ... provokes comparison with Millais's better-knit and more dramatic *The Knight Errant.*"

Millais's picture (Tate Gallery) was exhibited at the Royal Academy in 1870 with an accompanying note in the catalogue explaining that the order of Knights errant existed "to protect widows and orphans, and to succour maidens in distress." It seems to have been the obvious source for Dicksee's *Chivalry*, although in Millais's painting the villain has apparently

succeeded in his dastardly undertaking and left the scene before the arrival of the knight, while in Dicksee's the maiden is saved in the nick of time. Behind both works lies a long tradition of pictures of knights rescuing ladies in subjects such as *St. George and the Dragon*. The importance Victorians attributed to the virtue of chivalry is indicated by the fact that *The Spirit of Chivalry*, along with *Religion* and *Justice*, was one of three subjects initially selected in 1844 to be painted in fresco in the House of Lords in the new Palace of Westminster (see Appendix II). In the actual fresco by Daniel Maclise, conspicuous among the figures paying homage to the ideal is a knight in armor who draws a sword inscribed "A Dieu et aux Dames."

Provenance

Commissioned by Sir John Aird, Hyde Park Terrace, 1885 (Sale: Christie's London, May 3, 1935, Lot 52, £94 10s).
Anon. Sale: Parke-Bernet, New York, February 24, 1971, Lot 18, reproduced.

Exhibitions

Royal Academy, 1885, No. 53.

References

Art Journal, 1885, p. 258.
The Illustrated London News, May 9, 1885, p. 481, reproduced p. 495.
Sydney Hodges, "Mr. Frank Dicksee, ARA," *Magazine of Art*, Vol. X, 1887, pp. 216-222.
Art Journal, 1891, pp. 138-139, reproduced p. 138 (description of Aird's home).
A. G. Temple, *The Art of Painting in the Queen's Reign*, London, 1897, p. 206.
E. Rimbault Dibdin, "Frank Dicksee, RA," *Art Annual: Supplement to the Art Journal*, 1905, pp. 9, 28, 32.
Auction, February, 1971, reproduced p. 19 (sale notice).

J. E. Millais, *The Knight Errant*
(The Tate Gallery, London)

D. Maclise, *The Spirit of Chivalry*
(British Crown copyright, reproduced with permission of the Controller of Her Britannic Majesty's Stationery Office)

10. F. Dicksee, *Chivalry*.
(*see color Plate III, p. 161*)

WILLIAM DYCE, RA
(1806-1864)

was born in Aberdeen on the 19th of September, 1806. At the age of 13, he entered Marischal College in Aberdeen, where for four years he studied medicine and theology. In secret he also drew and painted. While his reputation today rests on his achievements as an artist, he was also accomplished in a number of other fields. He never lost interest in theology, and he became a leader of the High Church movement and wrote a number of essays on ecclesiastical matters. He wrote music, and in 1829 won a prize for a treatise on magnetism.

His early knowledge of art was derived from prints after the works of artists including Raphael, Domenichino, Poussin and Albani. In 1824 he overcame parental opposition to becoming a painter when, on a brief visit to London, he received some encouragement from the President of the Royal Academy, Sir Thomas Lawrence (1769-1830). He then studied at the Royal Academy Schools for a few months and in 1825 made the first of four visits to Italy. There he was particularly impressed with the work of Titian and Poussin. The following year he made his debut at the Royal Academy with *Bacchus Nursed by the Nymphs of Nysa.*

In 1827, on his second trip to Rome, he came under the influence of the German Nazarene painters. From them and from his own study of early Italian art, he became acquainted with fresco techniques. Seventeen years later he was able to put this knowledge to good use when the project of decorating the new Palace of Westminster with frescoes was begun (see Appendix II). In August, 1845, he received a formal commission to decorate the space behind the throne in the House of Lords. During the decade and a half prior to this, he established himself first as Aberdeen's, then as Edinburgh's leading portrait painter. He also made a third trip to Italy, was appointed Master of the Trustees Academy in Edinburgh, and on behalf of the Council of the London School of Design made a trip to Prussia, Bavaria, Saxony, and France to study the application of design to manufactures. From 1838 to 1843, he held the post of Superintendent of the Schools of Design in London. He was elected an Associate member of the Royal Academy in 1844.

Dyce's German connections brought him to the attention of H. R. H. Prince Albert, who was serving as the head of the committee responsible for the decoration of the new Houses of Parliament. This exposure resulted in several Royal commissions including a fresco for the Garden Pavilion at Buckingham Palace (see Appendix II); another very large fresco for Osborne House entitled *Neptune Resigning to*

Britannia the Empire of the Sea (see No. 11); and two religious paintings, *Madonna and Child* and *St. Joseph,* which were also intended for Osborne House.

Dyce's clean lined, Nazarene-inspired style helped make him sympathetic to the early work of the Pre-Raphaelites, and it was he who first persuaded John Ruskin (1819-1900) to look at their work. The critic was so won over that in 1855, he attacked Dyce's *Christabel* (Glasgow Art Gallery) as a false branch of Pre-Raphaelitism which was limited to imitating the style of old religious masters. Dyce did then turn more to direct observation of nature and his *Titian's First Essay in Colour* (Aberdeen Art Gallery), exhibited at the Royal Academy in 1857, won high praise from Ruskin. During his later life, much of Dyce's energies were taken up by the frescoes for the Queen's Robing Room in the Palace of Westminster. Five of the seven panels planned for this room were completed when Dyce died at Streatham near London in 1864.

From 1827 until he stopped showing in 1861, Dyce exhibited only forty-one works at the Royal Academy, several of which were studies for his fresco commissions. He became a full Academician in 1848 and was considered for the presidency of the Academy in 1850, but declined to have his name put forward in opposition to Charles Eastlake (q.v.).

Bibliography
James Dafforne, "British Artists: Their Style and Character; No. LI — William Dyce," *Art Journal,* 1860, pp. 293-296.
James Stirling Dyce, "The Life, Correspondence, and Writings of William Dyce, RA 1806-1864," unpublished typescript by Dyce's son in the Aberdeen Art Gallery.
Austin Chester, "The Art of William Dyce, RA," *Windsor Magazine,* 1909, pp. 576-590.
Quentin Bell, *The Schools of Design,* London, 1963, pp. 79-83.
Allen Staley, "William Dyce and Outdoor Naturalism." *Burlington Magazine,* November, 1963, pp. 470-476.
Charles Carter, *Centenary Exhibition of the Work of William Dyce, RA, 1806-1864,* Aberdeen Art Gallery and Thos. Agnew & Sons, London, 1964, (exhibition catalogue).

11. * NEPTUNE RESIGNING TO BRITANNIA THE EMPIRE OF THE SEA

Oil on paper laid down on board: 12-1/2 x 19-1/4 inches

This small picture was Dyce's only work in the Royal Academy exhibition of 1847. It was accompanied in the catalogue by an explanatory note: "Sketch for a picture to be painted at Osborne House for Her Majesty and H.R.H. Prince Albert." Dyce had completed his *Baptism of King Ethelbert,* the first of the frescoes to be painted in the new Houses of Parliament, in August 1846. In the same month he received a royal commission to paint a large fresco in Osborne House, the Italianate villa which Prince Albert had designed as a holiday residence on the Isle of Wight overlooking the harbors of Southampton and Portsmouth. Dyce initially proposed a subject from Boccaccio, but his royal patrons chose the subject of Neptune because Osborne was the "Marine Residence"

(continued on page 148)

W. Dyce, *Neptune Resigning to Britannia the Empire of the Sea* — fresco (British Crown copyright, reproduced with permission of the Controller of Her Britannic Majesty's Stationery Office)

11. W. Dyce, *Neptune Resigning to Britannia the Empire of the Sea.*
(*see color Plate IV, p. 162*)

SIR CHARLES LOCK EASTLAKE, PRA

(1793-1865)

was born in Plymouth on November 18, 1793, the son of a well-to-do lawyer. As a boy, he accompanied the painter in watercolors Samuel Prout (1783-1852) on sketching trips in the countryside around Plymouth and received some instruction from him. At the age of 14, he was sent to the Charterhouse School in London, but a year later, he left that institution to study under Benjamin Robert Haydon (1786-1846). He then entered the Schools of the Royal Academy where he was instructed by the Keeper, the Swiss-born painter Henry Fuseli (1741-1825). In 1814 he was sent to Paris by his first patron, Jeremiah Herman, to copy in the Louvre, but his stay was cut short by the return of the Emperor Napoleon from Elba. Eastlake hastened back home where he began to earn his living painting portraits. The landing of *H.M.S. Bellerophon* at Portsmouth en route to St. Helena provided the young artist with his most prominent sitter. His portrait of Napoleon was the last painted in Europe during Napoleon's lifetime. The proceeds from the sale of this picture and replicas enabled Eastlake to visit Italy in 1816 and Greece in 1818. On the latter trip he was accompanied by the architect Charles Barry (1795-1860), who was to design the new Houses of Parliament two decades later. From 1818 to 1830 Eastlake resided in Rome.

Eastlake made his debut at the Academy's Summer Exhibition in 1823 with three Roman views, and four years later he was elected an Associate member of the Royal Academy. In 1830 he became a full Academician, and in 1842 he was named the Academy's Librarian. He resigned this post in 1844 when he was appointed secretary to the Royal Commission for the Decoration of the Houses of Parliament (see Appendix II). At this time he was commissioned by Prince Albert to execute a fresco illustrating Milton's *Comus* for the garden pavilion at Buckingham Palace (see Appendix II). He exhibited an oil version of this work at the Academy in 1845. Five years later he was elected to succeed Martin Archer Shee (1769-1850) as President of the Royal Academy. Eastlake's official duties encroached increasingly on his time, and, after he was appointed Director of the National Gallery in 1855, he ceased to exhibit at the Royal Academy, having shown only fifty-one works there since his first appearance in 1823.

In addition to being an artist and an administrator, Eastlake was also an author whose *oeuvre* varied from a translation of Goëthe's *Farbenlehre* to his own *Materials for a History of Oil Painting*. In 1865 despite ill health, Eastlake insisted on taking his annual trip to the Continent. He became seriously ill in Milan and then on December 24, (a slight improvement in his condition having permitted his continuing to Pisa) he suffered a relapse and died.

Bibliography

"Portraits of British Artists; No. 1—Charles Lock Eastlake, RA," *Art Union*, 1847, p. 96.
"British Artists: Their Style and Character; No. IX—Sir Charles Lock Eastlake, KB, PRA," *Art Journal*, 1855, pp. 277-280.
Lady Eastlake, *A Memoir of Sir Charles L. Eastlake*, London, 1869.
W. Monkhouse, *Pictures by Sir Charles L. Eastlake*, London, 1875.
Allan Cunningham, *Lives of the Most Eminent British Painters*, London, 1879-1880, Vol. III, pp. 308-324, (revised edition, annotated and continued to the present time by Mrs. Charles Heaton).

12. * THE SALUTATION TO THE AGED FRIAR

Oil on canvas: 37-1/4 x 44-1/2 inches

Eastlake first began to paint Italian genre subjects such as this while living in Rome in the 1820s, following the lead of the Swiss artist Léopold Robert (1794-1835). However, in 1830 he left Rome to live in England, so this picture, exhibited a decade after his return, was probably painted in England. The subject is imaginative, based on memories rather than direct observation, and the reverence of the peasants toward the old friar introduces an element of moralizing sentimentality which seems to be a reflection of mid-century Victorian religious piety.

The Salutation to the Aged Friar was the only work contributed by Eastlake to the Academy exhibition of 1840. It was well received, and it continued to be praised by critics throughout Eastlake's career. In *Fraser's Magazine*, William Makepeace Thackeray wrote extravagantly,

> Now, it would be very easy to find fault with this picture. . . . But . . . the merits of the performance incomparably exceed them. . . . What a tender grace and purity in the female heads! . . . indeed, I don't know in any painter, ancient or modern, such a charming character of female beauty. . . . There is no affectation of middle-age mannerism. . . . The picture is truly Catholic — having about it what the hymn calls 'solemn mirth,' and giving the spectator the utmost possible pleasure in viewing it.

The critic of the *Art Union* lyricized:

> It is of the very highest merit; exquisite in composition and admirable in execution . . .

touching in the extreme; the production is one that cannot fail to produce pleasure; those who may not be able to appreciate its character as an example of art, will at all events, feel the sweet story it tells and enjoy it as a refreshing transcript of true nature. It is on the whole, the favorite of the year; it is impossible for language to overpraise it.

Comparing it to *The Slave Trade* by François Auguste Biard (1799 (?)-1882) which was also in the Academy exhibition of 1840, H. F. Chorley, writing for the *Athenaeum*, stated that *The Salutation to the Aged Friar* "steals into the mind like a hymn of thanksgiving after the riot of a demon's sabbath."

When the engraving after the picture was reviewed in the *Art Journal* in 1852, *The Salutation to the Aged Friar* was described as forming "an excellent companion to Eastlake's picture of *Pilgrims in Sight of Rome.*" The latter work, exhibited at the Royal Academy in 1828 and of which Eastlake painted six replicas, was one of his first great public successes. The *Art Journal* turned again to *The Salutation to the Aged Friar* in 1855 in a biography of Eastlake which described the painting as being "one of the great attractions of the year 1840; . . . a touching incident, gracefully illustrated."

Provenance

Sir Francis Graham Moon, Bart., London (Sale: Christie's, London, April 12, 1872, Lot 195, £ 435 15 s.).
Thomas Agnew & Sons, London.
Edward Herman, M.P.
Anon Sale: Sotheby's Belgravia, London, June 4, 1974, Lot 122, reproduced.
Fine Art Society, London (Agents).

Exhibitions

Royal Academy, 1840, No. 61.

References

Art Union, May, 1840, p.73.
Athenaeum, May 16, 1840, pp. 400-402.
[William Makepeace Thackeray], "A Pictorial Rhapsody by Michael Angelo Titmarsh with an introductory letter to Mr. Yorke," *Fraser's Magazine*, June, 1840. (reprinted in *The Paris Sketchbook and Art Criticisms*, The Oxford Thackeray, Vol. II, p. 503).
Art Journal, 1852, p. 131.
"British Artists: Their Style and Character, No. IX—Sir Charles Lock Eastlake, KB, PRA," *Art Journal*, 1855, p. 278.

Forthcoming References

David Robertson, *Sir Charles Eastlake and the Victorian Art World*, Princeton University Press, 1975 (?) Fig. 23, Appendix A.

12. C. L. Eastlake, *The Salutation to the Aged Friar.*
(*see color Plate V, p. 163*)

AUGUSTUS LEOPOLD EGG, RA
(1816-1863)

was the son of a prominent gunmaker of Piccadilly, where he was born on May 2, 1816. While attending school in Kent, he showed no particular inclination or talent for drawing, and it was not until 1834 that he took up painting and entered Sass's Academy. The following year, he enrolled in the Royal Academy Schools, and in 1838 he made his debut at the Academy's annual exhibition with a small work entitled *A Spanish Girl*. Just prior to this first appearance on the Academy's walls, however, in the year of Queen Victoria's accession, 1837, Egg banded together with several fellow students in the group known as The Clique (see Appendix I). At this time Egg, according to an acquaintance, John Imray, reminiscing in the *Art Journal* some sixty years later, thought his field should be "illustrations of famous works."

Egg's Academy exhibits, derived mainly from English sixteenth- and seventeenth-century history and English literature, especially Shakespeare, met with success, and by 1847 he was described by a critic as one of the foremost astists of the English school. A year later he was elected as an Associate of the Royal Academy. Along with William Dyce (q.v.), Egg was among the first established artists to support and encourage the Pre-Raphaelites. He agreed to purchase William Holman Hunt's *Claudio and Isabella* after the commission had been repudiated by another Academician, and his work may have had some influence on various members of the Pre-Raphaelite Brotherhood. In turn their work may have influenced his later productions, especially his tragic trilogy of an unfaithful Victorian wife exhibited at the Royal Academy in 1858 (Tate Gallery).

Egg was elevated to the rank of full Academician in 1861, but he last exhibited at the Academy in 1860. His health was always delicate, and he spent most of 1861 and 1862 in Algiers in order to benefit from the climate. He visited England briefly in 1862 and then returned to Algiers, where he died on March 25, 1863. During his short career he exhibited twenty-eight works at the Royal Academy.

Bibliography

"Portraits of British Artists; No. 8—Augustus Leopold Egg," *Art Union*, 1847, p. 312.
Art Journal, 1863, p. 87 (obituary).
"Notes on the Life of Augustus L. Egg," *The Reader, A Review of Literature, Science and Art*, 1863, pp. 462, 486-487, 557-558; new vol., pp. 42-43, 91, 516-517.
Peter Ferriday, "Augustus Egg," *The Architectural Review*, CXXXIV, 1963, pp. 420-422.
Frederick Cummings and Allen Staley, *Romantic Art in Britain: Paintings and Drawings, 1760-1860*, Philadelphia Museum of Art, 1968, pp. 283-284 (exhibition catalogue).

13. *MADAME DE MAINTENON AND SCARRON — SKETCH FOR A PICTURE

Oil on panel: 9 x 11-1/4 inches
Inscribed, lower left: *Augustus Egg, 1847*

Madame de Maintenon and Scarron was listed in the Royal Academy catalogue of 1859 with the quotation "She rejects the wealth of a fool, for a man of talent." Mme. de Maintenon (1635-1719), who was to become the governess of Louis XIV's children in 1669 and eventually the wife of the King, was born Françoise d'Aubigné. Her first marriage, in 1651, was to the poet, dramatist, novelist, and famous wit, Paul Scarron (1610-1660), who was miserably deformed from rheumatism as well as much older than his bride. However, since she was from an impoverished family, and hence without many prospects, the marriage was advantageous, and it put her at the center of France's most brilliant literary society.

Superficially, the little panel is reminiscent of the work of Charles Robert Leslie (q.v.), whose charming and humorous recreations of moments in history and literature amused Englishmen throughout the first half of the nineteenth century. Egg's pictures, on the other hand, despite their physical similarities to Leslie's work, tend to moralize rather than amuse. This is very much the case with *Madame de Maintenon and Scarron* as can be seen in the quotation from the Academy catalogue. The theme of rejection had been taken up by Egg in 1846 in his *Buckingham Rebuffed* (RA, 1846), which may have served as a source of inspiration for this panel executed in the following year. That Egg wanted the moral impact of Mme. de Maintenon's preference for the ugly but talented Scarron made clear, can be seen from a letter he wrote to Peter Potter (*Forbes* Magazine Collection), the man for whom the panel was painted. In it he declared: "The 'Madame de Maintenon' one especially wants the figure of Scarron (who was a little humpbacked man) to be more fully carried out to tell the story more plainly."

The figure of Scarron would have been "more fully carried out" had the sketch been worked up into a completed work. It is noteworthy that Egg exhibited this sketch — frankly catalogued as a sketch — rather than a completed work at the Royal Academy. It is probably indicative of the declining state of his health that he should choose to exhibit in 1859 a work, and a relatively unimportant one at that, some twelve years after it had been executed.

Provenance
Peter Potter
G. R. Burnett
L. V. Flatou (Sale: Christie's, London, March 23, 1861, Lot 88 and Christie's London, May 2, 1868, Lot 62).
J. S. Maas & Co., Ltd., London.

Exhibitions
Royal Academy, 1859, No. 166.
The Art and Mind of Victorian England: Paintings from the Forbes Magazine Collection, University Gallery, University of Minnesota, Minneapolis, 1974, No. 10 (reproduced in catalogue).

References
The Illustrated London News, May 21, 1859, p. 498.
Michael A. Findlay, "Forbes Saves the Queen," *Arts Magazine*, February, 1973, p. 27.
Melvin Waldfogel, "Introduction," *The Art and Mind of Victorian England: Paintings from the Forbes Magazine Collection*, University Gallery, University of Minnesota, Minneapolis, 1974, pp. 19, 21-22. (exhibition catalogue).
"Victorian Art and Mind," *Apollo*, December, 1974, p. 527.

Two autograph letters from the artist to Peter Potter discussing the picture are fixed to the back of the panel:

Ivy Cottage
Sept._____

Dear Sir,
I have sent you the sketches per post. Should you like either of them I should be very happy to finish it for you. The "Madame de Maintenon" one especially wants the figure of Scarron (who was a little humpbacked man) to be more fully carried out to tell the story more plainly, which I can easily do by painting on it a little more.

I remain Sir
Your obedient _____
Augustus Egg

Peter Potter, Esq.

Ivy Cottage

My Dear Sir,
I have at last completed the sketches, and will send it _____ by this night train, and hope that _____ which I have done to it will meet with your approbation. I should be glad if you would let me know at your earliest convenience, how you like it.

I remain,
Faithfully yours,
Augustus Egg

Peter Potter, Esq.

13. A. L. Egg, *Madame de Maintenon and Scarron — Sketch for a Picture.*

WILLIAM ETTY, RA
(1787-1849)

was born the seventh child of a baker in York on March 18, 1787. At age eleven, he was apprenticed to Robert Peck, publisher of the *Hull Packet*, a weekly newspaper. For the next seven years he set type, and read and drew in his spare time. In 1806 he moved to London and was accepted as a probationer in the Royal Academy Schools, where in the following year he became a full student. He also studied under the greatest British portrait painter of the period, Sir Thomas Lawrence (1769-1830), and in 1816 he worked briefly in Paris under the French painter Jean-Baptiste Regnault (1754-1829). He made his debut at the Academy's annual exhibition in 1811 but it was not until 1821, when he exhibited *Cleopatra's Arrival in Cilicia,* that he was able to make a name for himself. The success of this picture enabled him to work in Rome and Venice from 1822 to 1824. He was elected an Associate of the Royal Academy in 1824 and a full Academician four years later. Between 1811 and 1850 he exhibited one hundred and thirty-eight works there.

Etty was devoted to the human figure and refused to stop attending the life school after he became a member of the Academy. He owned a large collection of engravings after the works of Raphael, Titian, Poussin and Rubens, and his coloring and freedom of handling are often reminiscent of Rubens. Although Etty's oil sketches of female nudes were not exhibited publicly, he incorporated them in more acceptable scenes of classical history and mythology.

In 1843 he received a commission from Prince Albert to execute a fresco in the Garden Pavilion at Buckingham Palace (see Appendix II). His lack of experience with the medium caused the result to be so unsuccessful that the commission was taken away and given to William Dyce. Despite this setback, Etty's career flourished. When he died in York on November 13, 1849, his estate totaled £17,000, a very large sum at the time.

Bibliography

William Etty, Society of Arts, London, 1849, pp. 13, 37-40.
Alexander Gilchrist, *Life of William Etty, R.A.,* 2 Vols., London, 1855.
Allan Cunningham, *Lives of the Most Eminent British Painters,* London, 1879-1880, Vol. III, pp. 294-307 (revised edition, annotated and continued to the present time by Mrs. Charles Heaton).
William Gaunt and F. Gordon Roe, *Etty and the Nude,* Leigh-on-Sea, 1943.
James M. Biggins, *Etty and York,* York, 1949.
Dennis Farr, *William Etty,* London, 1958.

14. PHAEDRIA AND CYMOCHLES ON THE IDLE LAKE

Oil on Canvas: 23-1/2 x 31-1/4 inches

This is the second of two versions of this subject, which Etty exhibited at the Royal Academy in 1832 and 1835. The earlier picture is now in the Art Museum, Princeton University. Both pictures were inspired by Book II, Canto 6, of *The Faery Queene* by Edmund Spencer, although in the catalogues of the Royal Academy exhibitions each was accompanied by a quotation of different lines. Those printed in the earlier year describe the boat, which is much the same in both pictures:

> Along the shore as swift as glance of eye,
> A little gondelay, bedecked trim
> With boughs and arbours woven cunningly
> That like a little forest seemed outwardly.

In this second version, there are numerous changes in detail, and the lines quoted seem to have been chosen to emphasize these changes:

> And all the way the wanton damsel found
> New mirth her passenger to entertaine,
> For she in pleasaunt perpose did abound
> And greatly joyed merrye tales to sayne.

> And other whiles vaine toyes she would devize
> As her fantastic wit did most delight,
> Sometimes her head she fondly would aguize
> With gaudy girlondes, or fresh flowrets dight
> About her neck, or rings of rushes plight.

The most conspicuous addition is the figure of Cupid standing by Phaedria's knee. Whereas in the earlier version Cymochles is on his knees facing Phaedria, here they are seated side by side in the stern of the boat. A rudder held by Phaedria in the earlier picture has been replaced by a garland of flowers trailing in the water. A pair of love birds nestles in the branches above the figures, and there are many other slight additions or changes.

Gilchrist describes Etty's borrowing back from his cousin Thomas Bodley a study of the summer sea made at Brighton in order to paint the background. Preparatory drawings are in the Witt Collection and in the Victoria and Albert Museum. The theme of voluptuous eroticism is characteristic of Etty.

Provenance

Charles P. Matthews (Sale: Christie's, London, June 6, 1891, Lot 28, 200 gns.).
Thomas Agnew & Sons, London
Huth Collection
Mr. Cyril Flower
Lady Battersea, his wife.
Thomas Alden Thorp, bought 1920.
Brig. R. W. C. Britten, M.C. (Sale: Sotheby's, London, February 18, 1970, Lot 120, reproduced).
M. Newman Ltd., London

W. Etty, *Phaedria and Cymochles on the Idle Lake*
(The Art Museum, Princeton University)

14. W. Etty, *Phaedria and Cymochles on
the Idle Lake.*
(*see color Plate VI, p. 164*)

Exhibitions

Royal Academy, 1835, No. 310.

The Art and Mind of Victorian England: Paintings from the Forbes Magazine Collection, University Gallery, University of Minnesota, Minneapolis, 1974, No. 11 (reproduced in catalogue).

References

The Times, May 23, 1835.

Alexander Gilchrist, *Life of William Etty, RA,* London, 1855, Vol. II, pp. 28, 338.

William Gaunt and F. Gordon Roe, *Etty and the Nude,* Leigh-on-Sea, 1943, p. 96.

Dennis Farr, *William Etty,* London, 1958, pp. 68, 72-73, 151, No. 78.

Thomas L. Sloane, *"Phaedria and Cymochles on the Idle Lake," Record of the Art Museum: Princeton University,* XXVII, No. 2, 1968, pp. 81-83 (Princeton version).

Michael Findlay, "Forbes Saves the Queen," *Arts Magazine,* February, 1973, p. 27.

Muriel Freeman, "Kinetic Art in the Forbes Collection," *New Jersey Music & Arts,* September, 1974, reproduced p. 35 (gallery view, see upper left corner).

Melvin Waldfogel, "Introduction," *The Art and Mind of Victorian England: Paintings from the Forbes Magazine Collection,* University Gallery, University of Minnesota, Minneapolis, 1974, p. 20 (exhibition catalogue).

According to a note on the back of the picture, Etty presented the study to the owner of the horse, Joseph Rickman, who was introduced to him by a mutual friend while Etty was sketching the horse in the Strand.

Provenance

Joseph Rickman
James Rickman, Stockwell, his son.
Anon. Sale: Christie's, London, April 26, 1974, Lot 186.
Fine Art Society, London (Agents).

15. A CARTHORSE

Oil on panel transferred to canvas:
19-1/4 x 23-1/4 inches
Original frame

This sketch of a piebald horse served as a study for Etty's *Pluto Carrying Off Proserpine* which was exhibited at the Royal Academy in 1839. Although animal painting, especially of horses and dogs, was a tradition strongly established in British art, the appearance of a horse in Etty's *oeuvre* is unusual. Etty was devoted to the study of the human body and even after being elected an Academician, he still continued to attend the life classes at the Academy School.

In *Pluto Carrying Off Proserpine,* "That fair field of Enna where Proserpine gathering flowers, herself a fairer flower, by Gloomy Dis was gathered," the horse, harnessed with two others to Pluto's chariot, is seen rearing on the left side of the canvas. As would be expected in an Etty, however, nude human figures dominate the composition. It is not surprising, therefore, that no mention was made of the horse in the review of *Pluto* and *Proserpine* which appeared in the *Art Union* (1839, p. 69).

W. Etty, *Pluto Carrying Off Proserpine*

15. W. Etty, *A Carthorse.*

SIR LUKE FILDES, RA
(1844-1927)

was born in Liverpool on October 18, 1844. He was christened Samuel Luke but was persuaded by his friend, the journalist, George Augustus Sala, to drop the Samuel when he began exhibiting. He first studied at the Mechanics Institute in Liverpool and then at Warrington School of Art. After three years there, he moved to London in 1863 and began studying at the South Kensington Schools. Eventually, he entered the Royal Academy Schools. In 1868, he made his debut at that institution's annual Summer Exhibition with a work entitled *Nightfall*. Prior to this, to earn his living while he resided in London, Fildes worked as an illustrator for *The Graphic* and other publications. An introduction by John Everett Millais (q.v.) brought Fildes's work to the attention of Charles Dickens who commissioned him to illustrate his last novel, *Edwin Drood*. Working for *The Graphic*, a periodical interested in social observation, had an important effect on Fildes, whose reputation today rests largely on social realist pictures beginning with *Applicants for Admission to a Casual Ward* (Royal Holloway College, Egham), first exhibited at the Academy in 1874 and derived from an earlier engraving entitled *Houseless and Hungry*. It was followed by *The Widower* (RA, 1876), *The Return of the Penitent* (RA, 1879), and *The Doctor* (RA, 1891; Tate Gallery). *Applicants* established Fildes as an up-and-coming artist. He was elected an Associate Academician in 1879 and in 1887, a full Academician.

Fildes's social conscience was defused by a trip to Italy in 1875 with his wife, the sister of the painter Henry Woods (1846-1921), during which he became much attracted to Venice. His academy pictures during the 1880s were principally of Venetian subjects. In the late '80s and early '90s, he turned increasingly to portraiture. It was as a practitioner of this genre that Fildes enjoyed his greatest financial success. His portrait of the Princess of Wales, later Queen Alexandra, painted in 1894, was very well received and led to a number of Royal commissions, including the first state portrait of King Edward VII (RA, 1902). He was knighted in 1906, and in 1912, was commissioned to paint the first state portrait of King George V. Prior to his death in 1927, Fildes exhibited one hundred and fifty-eight works at the Royal Academy.

Bibliography

W. W. Fenn, "Luke Fildes, ARA," in *Some Modern Artists and Their Work*, ed. Wilfrid Meynell, London, 1883, pp. 103-109.

David Croal Thomson, "The Life and Work of Luke Fildes, RA," *Art Annual: Supplement to the Art Journal*, 1895.

L. V. Fildes, *Luke Fildes, RA: A Victorian Painter*, London, 1968.

16. BETTY

Oil on canvas: 12-1/2 x 8-3/4 inches
Inscribed, lower right: *Luke Fildes to G. A. S. '75*

This picture is a replica of the work contributed by Fildes to the Royal Academy exhibition of 1875 (No. 1221). It was painted for and is inscribed to his friend and patron, the writer George Augustus Sala.

Fildes had his first great success at the Royal Academy in 1874 with his *Applicants for Admission to a Casual Ward*. Following a trip to the Continent, during which he visited Paris, he was married on July 15, 1874, and during the latter part of the summer he lived with his new bride at Goring-on-Thames near Oxford. There he began a picture of his wife which, according to the artist's son, he intended to paint entirely out-of-doors and to exhibit the following year as *The Milkmaid*. The couple spent the winter of 1874-75 in Paris, and Fildes completed the picture in a studio there. He attempted to use French models, but after dismissing them all as "undersized dirty drabs," he reverted to his original sitter. As Mrs. Fildes's name was Fanny, the reason why *The Milkmaid* became *Betty* when sent to the Royal Academy in the spring of 1875 is unclear.

Fildes's intention to paint the picture entirely out-of-doors recalls earlier efforts by artists such as Ford Madox Brown (1821-1893) to do the same thing in the 1850s. However, since he began the picture after a visit to the Continent and completed it in Paris, it seems likely that the artist was influenced by contemporary French *plein-air* painting. The pronounced brush-stroke in *Betty* has more in common with the *facture* of contemporary French art than with the stippled precision of the Pre-Raphaelites. Although Fildes's son denied that the artist ever was much of an admirer of contemporary French painting, *Betty* does seem to be a forerunner of the wave of French influence which was to be a major element in progressive English painting of the 1880s.

When the first version of *Betty* appeared at the Royal Academy, it received favorable, if not long, notices in the *Art Journal* (1875, p. 252), *The Illustrated London News* (May 22, 1875, pp. 486-487), and in Henry Blackburn's *Academy Notes* (1875, p. 53). Despite the fact that, according to his son, Fildes did not think of *Betty* as one of his successes, it was selected by *The Illustrated London News* to be reproduced in color in its Christmas Supplement and by the *Art Journal* for a large plate in its *Art Annual* of 1895, which was devoted to Fildes.

In his letter of thanks to Fildes for this picture, Sala, discussing the artist's work in general, wrote:

> You bold young geniuses lash in your colour so audaciously that we weak-eyed fogies are puzzled, sometimes, to know whether there is any drawing underneath the paint at all. Well, you may say, Rembrandt painted with his thumb and Goya . . . painted the *Dos de Mayo* with a fork.

Provenance

Anon. Sale: Phillips, London, January 22, 1973, Lot P103.
Fine Art Society, London (Agents)

Exhibitions

The Art and Mind of Victorian England: Paintings from the Forbes Magazine Collection, University Gallery, University of Minnesota, Minneapolis, 1974, No. 12 (reproduced in catalogue).

References

L. V. Fildes, *Luke Fildes, RA: A Victorian Painter*, London, 1968, pp. 37, 41-42.

16. L. Fildes, *Betty*.

WILLIAM POWELL FRITH, RA

(1819-1909)

was born in Aldfield, Yorkshire, on January 9, 1819. His father "held a position of trust in the family of the then owner of Studley Royal, Mrs. Lawrence" (Frith, Vol. I, p. 1); however, in 1826, he became the proprietor of "The Dragon" Inn at Harrogate. He liked to draw and encouraged his son to do the same. When Frith junior was fifteen he stated his intention of becoming an auctioneer only to have his father urge him to become an artist. He was then sent to Sass's School of Art at No. 6 Charlotte Street, Bloomsbury, and finally entered the Royal Academy Schools. In 1837 Frith joined together with some fellow students in the group know as The Clique (see Appendix I). In 1840, he made his debut at the Academy with *Malvolio before the Countess Olivia*, an episode from Shakespeare's *Twelfth Night*. It was the first of some one hundred and forty-five works Frith exhibited at the Royal Academy before he stopped painting in 1902. His early work owed much, both in subject and style, to the lighthearted productions of Charles Robert Leslie (q.v.), but in 1854, he made an exciting departure in subject when he exhibited a large panorama of his fellow Victorians enjoying themselves on the beach at Ramsgate. *Life at the Seaside* (or *Ramsgate Sands* as it is frequently called) caused a sensation and was purchased by Queen Victoria herself. The Victorians enjoyed seeing themselves and their lifestyle immortalized on canvas and Frith's next opus in the genre, *Derby Day,* had to be protected with a rail when it was exhibited in 1858. Frith continued to produce successful pictures of contemporary life throughout his career. As he grew older, his style and coloring became drier and thinner, and he became rich and reactionary. In 1887 he published two volumes of memoirs. These were followed by a third volume a year later. He died at the age of ninety on November 2, 1909.

Bibliography

William Powell Frith, RA, *My Autobiography and Reminiscences,* 2 Vols., London, 1887.
William Powell Frith, RA, *Further Reminiscences,* London, 1888.
Jonathan Mayne, *An Exhibition of Paintings by William Powell Frith, RA, 1819-1909,* Corporation Art Gallery, Harrogate, and Whitechapel Art Gallery, London, 1951 (exhibition catalogue).

17. * 'FOR BETTER, FOR WORSE'

Oil on canvas: 61 x 49 inches
Inscribed, lower left: *W. P. Frith 1881*

Frith devoted a chapter to this painting in his memoirs. In it he describes the incident which inspired the picture: "an almost identical realization of it in Cleveland Square." He then goes on at great length to describe some of his sitters. The old Jew who posed for the bearded man to the left of the constable he had to pay ten shillings, "and some old clothes" for a three-hour sitting. The boy who posed for the young onlooker with his hands in his pockets fainted without notice, his hands never leaving his pockets. It was the monkey on the back of the young Italian boy in the right foreground which gave Frith the most difficulty, however. The creature delighted in jumping on his easel as well as attacking the picture itself. Afterwards, Frith wrote, "Little children are maddening; but commend me to the most terrible of those in preference to a monkey."

In the poignant juxtaposition of the affluent newlyweds about to enter their brougham, and the beggar and his wife and family behind it, lies the sentimental and moral *raison d'etre* for the title *'For Better, For Worse.'*

Provenance

Sir Frederick Wigan, Bart., Clare Lown, East Sheen (Sale: Christie's, London, December 9-10, 1915, Lot 72, £ 50 8s).
Sampson
Frost and Reed, London
Senator Andrew J. Sordoni, Jr., Wilkes-Barre, Pennsylvania (Sale: Parke-Bernet, New York, February 23, 1968, Lot 135, reproduced).

Exhibitions

Royal Academy, 1881, No. 14.
St. Jude's, Whitechapel, 1889, No. 7.
Victorian Art, The Emily Lowe Gallery, Hofstra University, Hempstead, New York, 1972, No. 69 (measurements given incorrectly in catalogue).

References

Art Journal, 1881, p. 185.
Henry Blackburn, *Academy Notes,* London, 1881, pp. 8-9, reproduced p. 9.
[Nestor], *Fun's Academy Skits,* London, 1881, pp. 17-19, reproduced p. 18.
"Our Guide to the Academy," *Punch,* May 7, 1881, p. 208.
The Illustrated London News, May 7, 1881, p. 459.
William Powell Frith, RA, *My Authobiography and Reminiscences,* New York, 1889, Vol. I, pp. 406-409.
Neville Wallis (ed.) *A Victorian Canvas: The Memoirs of W. P. Frith, RA,* London, 1957, pp. 154-156.
Art at Auction, London, 1968, p. 73, reproduced p. 73.
Michael A. Findlay, "Forbes Save the Queen," *Arts Magazine,* February, 1973, p. 26.
The Art and Mind of Victorian England: Paintings from the Forbes Magazine Collection, University Gallery, University of Minnesota, Minneapolis, 1974, pp. 10, 39 (exhibition catalogue).

Forthcoming References

Christopher Wood, *Victorian Panorama—Paintings of Victorian Life,* Faber & Faber, 1975 (?).

Fun's Academy Skits, 1881

No. 14.—SLIPPER-Y!

Punch, 1881

17. W. P. Frith, *'For Better, For Worse.'*
(*see color Plate VII, p. 165*)

18. * 'FOR BETTER, FOR WORSE'

Oil on canvas: 24-3/4 x 18-3/4 inches
Inscibed, lower left: *W. P. Frith. 1881.*

This painting is the oil sketch for the finished picture of the same title (see No. 17). It is probably the "sketched out composition of a wedding party" to which Frith refers in his memoirs while discussing the development of *'For Better, For Worse.'* It corresponds in composition and in all major details to the finished work, but the artist has still not fully visualized the characters who fill the various roles in the picture. While its greater freedom of handling has an appeal, the sketch is decidedly less interesting than the finished picture, in which the bearded Jew, the ragged sweeper, and the sailor-suited boy are all much more sharply characterized than their counterparts in the sketch. It was this ability to create the perfect type as well as compose large groups of people that assured Frith his place as the foremost contemporary genre painter of the period.

Provenance

Anon. Sale: Christie's, London, July 10, 1964, Lot 166.
M. Newman Ltd., London
Sir Edward Beharrell (Sale: Christie's, London, July 10, 1970, Lot 108, reproduced).

Exhibitions

19th Century Life, M. Newman Ltd., London, 1965, No. 16 (reproduced in catalogue).
The Art and Mind of Victorian England: Paintings from the Forbes Magazine Collection, University Gallery, University of Minnesota, Minneapolis, 1974, No. 14 (reproduced in catalogue).

References

William Powell Frith, RA, *My Autobiography and Reminiscences,* New York, 1889, Vol.I, p. 406.
Frank Davis, "The Victorian Scene," *The Illustrated London News,* March 6, 1965, p. 30, reproduced p. 30.
Michael A. Findlay, "Forbes Saves the Queen," *Arts Magazine,* February, 1973, p. 26.
Melvin Waldfogel, "Introduction," *The Art and Mind of Victorian England: Paintings from the Forbes Magazine Collection,* University Gallery, University of Minnesota, Minneapolis, 1974, p. 22 (exhibition catalogue).
Lyndel King, "Heroism began at home," *Art News,* November, 1974, p. 45.

19. GIRL HOLDING A PARASOL

Canvas laid on board in an oval mount:
10 x 8 inches
Original frame

This small sketch may have served as a study for Frith's *Derby Day,* exhibited at the Royal Academy in 1858 (Tate Gallery). It does not correspond exactly with any of the figures depicted in the finished picture, but the model closely resembles both a young lady in the carriage to the right of the center, reviewing the racing form with a friend, and the girl holding a parasol in the carriage to the extreme right being applied to by an impoverished old lady. Compositionally the latter figure is the closer to the sketch, the angle of the parasol and the downcast expression of the subject being the most conspicuous differences. The girl penciling her racing sheet is posed in a markedly different manner from the girl in the sketch, but apparently the same model was used for both.

In his *Reminiscences,* Frith recorded the following notation from his diary which may refer to this picture:

> February 9: 'First day's painting of *Racecourse.* Miss Mortimer sat. Did two heads of carriage-ladies pretty well.'

Frith also noted an amusing story about the ladies in the picture in general.

The owner [of *Derby Day*], Mr. Bell, was also very useful to me in procuring models. Few people have a more extensive acquaintance, especially among the female sex, than that possessed by Jacob Bell; and what seemed singular was the remarkable prettiness that distinguished nearly all these pleasant friends. I had but to name the points required, and an example was produced.

'What is it to be this time?' he would say. 'Fair or dark, long nose or short nose, Roman or aquiline, tall figure or small? Give your orders.'

The order was given, and obeyed in a manner that perfectly astonished me. I owe every female figure in the *Derby Day,* except two or three, to the foraging of my employer.

Derby Day was Frith's most successful painting and perhaps the most popular painting in England during the second half of the nineteenth century. When it was first exhibited at the Royal Academy, it required not only a rail but also two guards to protect it from the admiring crowds; and well into the twentieth century, it probably attracted larger crowds than any other painting in the National Gallery, where it first hung.

Provenance

Anon. Sale: Sotheby's Belgravia, London, October 30, 1973, Lot 211, reproduced.
Fine Art Society, London (Agents).

W. P. Frith, *Derby Day*—detail
(The Tate Gallery, London)

W. P. Frith, *Derby Day*—detail
(The Tate Gallery, London)

18. W. P. Frith, *'For Better, For Worse'* (sketch).

19. W. P. Frith, *Girl Holding a Parasol.*

SIR FRANCIS GRANT, PRA
(1803-1878)

was the fourth son of the Laird of Kilgraston, Perthshire, in Scotland. He was educated at Harrow and destined for a law career. Grant's early interest in art was strictly that of an amateur until he found himself in desperate financial straits, having run through his inheritance by the early 1830s. He settled in fox-hunting country at Melton Mowbray, Leicestershire, where he befriended the prominent sporting painter John Ferneley (1782-1860), who gave him some instruction. By 1834 Grant was proficient enough to have his *Breakfast Scene at Melton* included in the Academy exhibition of that year. This was a conversation piece showing a fashionable group of young aristocrats languidly breakfasting before the day's hunting. Its competent and flattering likenesses, painted in a relaxed style somewhat reminiscent of Romney and set in congenial and smart surroundings, established Grant as the favorite portaitist in early Victorian titled circles, and a list of the one hundred and fifty-three works which he exhibited at the Royal Academy from 1834 to 1879 reads like an abridged addition of the *Peerage*. He married a niece of the Duke of Rutland, and in 1856, exhibited a portrait of His Grace which according to the catalogue was commissioned and presented to the latter "by his tenantry." He painted Queen Victoria on several occasions although he never achieved the popularlity with her enjoyed by Edwin Landseer (q.v.) and Franz Xavier Winterhalter (1805-1873).

In 1841, he became an Associate Academician and in 1851, an Academician. Fifteen years later, upon the death of Charles Eastlake (q.v.), he was elected President of the Royal Academy after Edwin Landseer declined the post pleading ill health. He was knighted shortly afterwards. During his Presidency, the Academy moved to its present quarters in Burlington House. Grant declined an offer of burial in St. Paul's Cathedral, and, after his death in 1878, he was buried in Melton Church.

Bibliography

John Steegman, "Sir Francis Grant PRA: The Artist in High Society," *Apollo*, June, 1964, pp. 479-485.

Frederick Cummings and Allen Staley, *Romantic Art in Britain: Paintings and Drawings 1760-1860*, Philadelphia Museum of Art, pp. 255-256 (exhibition catalogue).

20. PORTRAIT OF GENERAL SIR JOSIAH CHAMPAGNE, G.C.H.

Oil on canvas: 50 x 40 inches
Inscribed, middle left: *On her Majesty's Service, General Sir Josiah Champagné GCH War Office*

This portrait of *General Sir Josiah Champagné, G.C.H.* appeared at the Royal Academy in 1836, only two years after Grant had first exhibited there. It is a very early picture, and, stylistically, is highly dependent upon the work of George Romney (1734-1802) and Sir Thomas Lawrence (1769-1830). In later works, such as the portraits of *Master James Keith Fraser on his Pony*, exhibited at the Royal Academy in 1845 (Mellon Collection) and *Miss Isabella Grant*, exhibited in 1850 (Leicester Museum and Art Gallery), Grant developed a distinctively Victorian combination of sentiment and charm. *General Sir Josiah Champagné, G.C.H.*, however, still sticks closely to an earlier style of portraiture without much hint of innovation.

The subject is depicted in general's uniform with the decorations of the Royal Hanoverian Guelphic Order, which was instituted by George III in 1815 and conferred only by the Hanoverian kings. (Thus it was no longer a British order after 1837). As a Knight of the Grand Cross of Hanover (G.C.H.), an honor he received in 1821, Sir Josiah wears a light blue sash and the silver eight-pointed star with the white horse of Hanover emblazoned in the center and with crossed swords of gold which signify his military division. Champagné died on January 31, 1840, after an extensive military career which included campaigns in the Revolutionary and Napoleonic Wars.

Provenance

Anon. Sale: Christie's, London, November 24, 1972, Lot 96.
Fine Art Society, London (Agents).

Exhibitions

Royal Academy, 1836, No. 554.
The Art and Mind of Victorian England: Paintings from the Forbes Magazine Collection, University Gallery, University of Minnesota, Minneapolis, 1974, No. 16 (reproduced in catalogue).

20. F. Grant, *Portrait of General Sir Josiah Champagné, G.C.H.*

KEELEY HALSWELLE

(1832-1911)

was born at Richmond, Surrey, in 1832. As an adolescent, he spent much of his spare time sketching along the banks of the Thames. Despite parental opposition, he was determined to become an artist, and, by way of a compromise, a position was found for him in an architect's office. This proved unsatisfactory, and Halswelle was allowed to work under an engraver and to study at the British Museum. During the early 1850s he began working for *The Illustrated London News,* and in 1854 (or 1855) he was sent by that journal to execute a series of sketches in Scotland. While in Edinburgh, he received several commissions for illustrations (including a set for the poems of Robert Herrick), and he decided to remain there. He continued his studies at the Schools of the Royal Scottish Academy and began exhibiting in Edinburgh in 1857.

Halswelle made his debut at the Royal Academy in London five years later with a modest work entitled *A Snow Storm.* Elected an Associate member of the Royal Scottish Academy in 1866, the artist went to Rome in 1868. Halswelle began his painting career as a landscape artist. In 1867 and 1868 he exhibited Scottish genre subjects at the Royal Academy; from 1869 to 1879 he exhibited mainly Italian genre scenes, but in 1877 and 1878 he changed to pictures of historical and literary subjects. Although these were quite successful (James Dafforne in the *Art Journal* of 1879 predicted that academic honors would soon be conferred on him), around 1880 Halswelle returned to landscapes, and in 1883 he published a book entitled *Six Years in a House-Boat,* a series of pictures of scenery along the Thames. His landscapes seem to have been popular, but before his death in Paris on April 11, 1911, Halswelle was neither elected an Associate member of the Royal Academy, where he had exhibited thirty-six works, nor a full Member of the Royal Scottish Academy, where he had often exhibited with success.

Bibliography

James Dafforne, "The Works of Keeley Halswelle, ARSA," *Art Journal,* 1879, pp. 49-52.
W. W. Fenn, "Keeley Halswelle, ARSA," *Magazine of Art,* Vol. IV, 1881, pp. 406-410.

21. THE PLAY SCENE IN HAMLET

Oil on canvas: 60 x 103 inches
Inscribed, lower left: *Keeley Halswelle, 1878*
Original frame

This painting was listed in the catalogue of the 1878 exhibition with the following verses from Act iii, Scene 2 of Shakespeare's *Hamlet:*

> 'Ham.   He poisons him i' the garden for his estate. His name's Gonzago: the story is extant, and written in very choice Italian: you shall see anon, how the murder gets the love of Gonzago's wife.
> Oph.   The king rises.
> Ham.   What, frightened with false fire!
> Queen   How fares my lord?
> Pol.   Give o'er the play.
> King   Give me some light: away!
> All.   Lights, lights, lights!'

Subjects inspired by Shakespeare's works were popular with nineteenth-century artists both in England and abroad. In the 1780s, Alderman John Boydell founded his Shakespeare Gallery. He persuaded many leading artists to paint pictures illustrating the dramatic works of Shakespeare and in 1803 published an ambitious book of engravings after them. However, the most famous English painting of *The Play Scene in Hamlet* is that of Daniel Maclise, exhibited at the Royal Academy in 1842 and now in the Tate Gallery (see No. 43).

James Dafforne compared the two versions in the *Art Journal* of 1879:

> Mr. Halswelle attempted a still higher flight in historical painting . . . and indeed it was a bold essay, seeing that Mr. Maclise's version of the same subject . . . is so well known. But the more recent composition bears no resemblance to its prototype. The *dramatis personae* are arranged somewhat differently, and thrown more into the background than those in Maclise's picture; the chamber wherein the drama is being acted is large, consequently the figures occupy a more extended space in the rear, leaving the foreground comparatively barren of interest. . . . The picture manifested a most successful advance beyond the artist's [Halswelle's] previous productions.

Reviews at the time the painting first appeared were more mixed but generally enthusiastic. The critic of the *Magazine of Art* complained, "Unfortunately a slight garishness or conventionality of color combine to prevent this powerful and intelligent composition from receiving full attention and justice." He admitted, however, that Halswelle "has never done a truly more dramatic work," and went on to acknowledge: "The artist has been particularly happy in his indications of the barbaric splendor of Elsinore, and the actions are throughout energetic." The reviewer for the *Art Journal* spoke of Halswelle's *The Play Scene in Hamlet* as "a large and most interesting work, rich in color, accessories and incident," but added that "the largeness of the chamber and

the wide space occupied by the *dramatis personae* may be objected to." He continued, however, by saying that these: "are not without certain compensating qualities, and it would be sorry criticism which would carp at possible shortcomings instead of rejoicing at positive achievement." Again in *The Illustrated London News,* the reviewer had mixed feelings about the picture:

> The varied emotion of the guilty Claudius, the amazed Queen, the bewildered Polonius, the innocent Ophelia, . . . are all very forcibly interpreted by Mr. Halswelle. The composition is very animated, and the light and shade skilfully [sic] balanced; but the work, in its entirety must be praised more on the score of its consummate draughtsmanship than of its pictorial adequacy It is a highly-colored tableau from an illustrated edition of Shakespeare; but it fails to fulfill all the requirements of the painter's art.

In 1881, W. W. Fenn, writing in the *Magazine of Art,* identified the setting as the seventh-century church of Santi Vincenzo ed Anastasio at the Abbazia delle Tre Fontane, the site where Saint Paul was said to have been executed, just outside of Rome. In the year that Halswelle went to Rome, the French Trappists took over the Abbazia, which had previously been deserted, and began its restoration. According to Fenn, although the church was "far removed from Elsinore, and erected two hundred years prior to the period of the great tragedy, Mr. Halswelle urges that it is in every way in accord with the tone and feeling of Shakespeare's masterpiece."

Punch, however, had the last word on Halswelle's *The Play Scene in Hamlet:* "Laboured: all work and no play. But 'Halswelle that ends well'—hem! Shakespere (sic)."

Provenance

Andrew G. Kurtz, Liverpool (Sale: Christie's, London, May 9, 1891, Lot 62, 250 gns.).
Thomas Clarke, Allerton Hall, Woolton, Liverpool (Sale: Christie's, London, January 29, 1926, Lot 31, £ 189).
Mrs. A. M. Matthews, granddaughter of Mr. Clarke (Sale: Christie's, London, November 20, 1970, Lot 279).

Exhibitions

Royal Academy, 1878, No. 936.
Loan Exhibition, Walker Art Gallery, Liverpool, 1886, No. 78.

References

Art Journal, 1878, pp. 149, 179.
Henry Blackburn, *Academy Notes,* London, 1878, reproduced p. 63.
Magazine of Art, 1878, Vol. I, p. 104.
The Illustrated London News, May 18, 1878, p. 458.

(continued on page 149)

21. K. Halswelle, *The Play Scene in Hamlet.*

EDITH HAYLLAR

(1860-1948)

was two years younger than her sister Jessica (q.v.) and an equally talented painter. Both were instructed by their father James Hayllar (1829-1920). Edith's work is similar both in style and subject to that of her older sister, and, for that matter, only differs from the pictures of her two younger sisters, Mary and Kate, by being slightly better painted. The common inspiration to the sisters were the comings and goings of the family in their rambling house, Castle Priory in Wallingford, Berkshire. One aspect of life there, which appealed to Edith more than to any of her sisters, was sports. She enjoyed painting not so much the actual game or event, but rather the moments of relaxation which followed. Boating, shooting, and tennis parties were among the activities of Victorian life which she meticulously and sympathetically recorded. In addition to showing twelve works at the Royal Academy from 1882 to 1897, Edith also exhibited at the Society of British Artists, the Institute of Oil Painters, and the Dudley Gallery. Around the turn of the century she married the Reverend Bruce MacKay and gave up painting. She never discussed her artistic career in later years, and her granddaughter was unaware that she had painted, until after her death in 1948.

Bibliography

Christopher Wood, "The Artistic Family Hayllar," Connoisseur, Part I: April, 1974, pp. 266-273; Part II: May, 1974, pp. 2-9.

22. * A SUMMER SHOWER

Oil on board: 21 x 17 inches
Inscribed, lower left: EDITH HAYLLAR 1883

A Summer Shower is one of Edith Hayllar's most delightful "sporting" pictures. Depicted is a tennis party taking refuge and refreshments in the hall of Castle Priory during a sudden summer rain. The picture demonstrates the high level of competence achieved in much ostensibly modest later Victorian genre painting. The verisimilitude with which the artist has depicted the reflection of rainy daylight on the figures and objects in the far room is particularly noteworthy. The face of the girl with the tennis racquet on her lap is reminiscent of the facial types used by William Powell Frith (q.v.), and the dryness of the handling also recalls that artist's later works.

A Summer Shower received no notices when it was first exhibited at the Royal Academy in

1883. Christopher Wood, however, in his article on the Hayllars, describes it as:

> One of the most charming genre scenes of the nineteenth century, a rustic, anglicised version of Tissot [q.v.]. It is wonderfully redolent of an English summer afternoon with sets of inconsequential tennis, showers, lemonade, and tea doubtless to follow.

Provenance

Anon. Sale: Christie's, London, July 10, 1970, Lot 60, reproduced.

Exhibitions

Royal Academy, 1883, No. 420.
The Art and Mind of Victorian England: Paintings from the Forbes Magazine Collection, University Gallery, University of Minnesota, Minneapolis, 1974, No. 17 (reproduced in color on cover of catalogue).

References

Christopher Wood, "The Great Victorian Painting Revival", Auction, November, 1970, p. 40, reproduced p. 41.

Christopher Wood, The Dictionary of Victorian Painters, London, 1971, p. 62, reproduced p. 283.

Michael A. Findlay, "Forbes Saves the Queen", Arts Magazine, February, 1973, p. 30, reproduced p. 27.

Christopher Wood, "The Artistic Family Hayllar", Connoisseur, Part I: April, 1974, reproduced p. 4, Part II: May, 1974, p. 6, reproduced p. 7 and in color on cover.

Melvin Waldfogel, "Introduction," The Art and Mind of Victorian England: Paintings from the Forbes Magazine Collection, University Gallery, University of Minnesota, Minneapolis, 1974, p. 22 (exhibition catalogue).

Sarah B. Sherrill, "Current and Coming, Victorian Painting," Antiques, September, 1974, reproduced p. 332.

"Major Exhibit to Key 'U' Victorian Festival," The Minneapolis Star, September 18, 1974, reproduced.

"A glimpse of Victoria's world," Minneapolis Tribune, September 22, 1974, reproduced.

Carole Nelson, "Exhibit wins respect for long-neglected Victorian paintings," St. Paul Sunday Pioneer Press, Family Life Section, September 29, 1974, p. 1, reproduced p. 1.

Lyndel King, "Heroism began at home," Art News, November, 1974, p. 45.

22. E. Hayllar, *A Summer Shower*.

JESSICA HAYLLAR
(1858-1940)

was born in 1858, one of nine children of the genre painter James Hayllar (1829-1920) and his wife, the former Ellen Cavell. Like her younger sisters Edith (q.v.), Kate, and Mary, Jessica was entirely instructed in painting by her father. Of the four she was the most prolific. All of them painted genre subjects, usually scenes of everyday life set in Castle Priory, Wallingford, the Hayllar residence in Berkshire from 1875 to 1899.

After moving from there to Bournemouth with her father, Jessica seems to have lost the source of her inspiration. She was crippled by an accident about this time and, although she continued to paint, her later works were confined almost exclusively to flower pictures.

A picture entitled *Going to "My Uncle's"* was accepted by the Royal Academy for inclusion in its Summer Exhibition in 1880. Over the next fifty years Jessica showed an additional thirty-nine pictures there.

Bibliography

Christopher Wood, "The Artistic Family Hayllar," *Connoisseur,* Part I: April, 1974, pp. 266-273; Part II: May, 1974, pp. 2-9.

order of execution, if not chronology, are *A Coming Event* (RA, 1886), *Fresh from the Font* (RA, 1887), *The Return from Confirmation* (RA, 1888), and *Fresh from the Altar* (RA, 1890). The concept was probably inspired by James Hayllar's popular *Miss Lilly* series of some twenty years earlier. Wood describes Jessica's four serial pictures as being among her "most ambitious and successful works." At the time of its exhibition at the Royal Academy in 1886, however, *A Coming Event* was unmentioned in any of the major reviews.

Provenance

Anon. Sale: Sotheby's Belgravia, London, April 23, 1974, Lot 97 reproduced.

Exhibitions

Royal Academy, 1886, No. 926.

References

Christopher Wood, "The Artistic Family Hayllar," *Connoisseur,* Part II, May, 1974, p. 5.

23. * A COMING EVENT

Oil on canvas: 22-1/2 x 18-1/2 inches
Inscribed, lower left: *Jessica Hayllar 1886*

Marriage, the ultimate relationship between men and women in Victorian eyes, was a subject often treated by artists of the period. Works dealing with the ceremony itself, or events immediately preceding or following it, range from *The Penny Wedding* (RA, 1819; Royal Collection) and *The Bride at Her Toilet* (RA, 1838; National Gallery of Scotland, Edinburgh) by David Wilkie (q.v.), to *Marriage Morning* (RA, 1844) by Richard Redgrave (q.v.), *Changing Homes* (RA, 1863) by George Elgar Hicks (b. 1824), *'For Better, For Worse'* by William Powell Frith (q.v., see Nos. 17 and 18), *The Health of the Bride* (RA, 1889; Tate Gallery) by Stanhope Forbes (1857-1947), and *A Wedding Morning* (Lady Lever Art Gallery, Port Sunlight) by John Henry F. Bacon (1868-1914). Among these works, however, there is no parallel to this treatment of an interior in which the trappings of things to come are evident without being overwhelming.

A Coming Event is, according to Christopher Wood, one of a cycle of four pictures. These in

23. J. Hayllar, *A Coming Event.*

JOHN ROGERS HERBERT, RA
(1810-1890)

was born at Maldon in Essex on January 23, 1810. From 1826 to 1828 he studied at the Royal Academy Schools and made his first appearance at the Academy's annual exhibition in 1830. He began his career painting portraits. In the mid-1830s he visited Italy where he came in contact with the German Nazarenes. At this time he began to paint romanticized subjects from Italian history or the poetry of Lord Byron and slowly to adopt a harder, drier style inspired by the Nazarenes, who were to have a pronounced influence upon his art in the 1840s. Upon his return to England he came increasingly under the influence of the architect Augustus Welby Northmore Pugin (1812-1852). Pugin was a convert to Catholicism, and following his lead, Herbert converted also about 1840. During the 1840s Herbert's art turned increasingly to religious subjects. His *Our Saviour Subject to His Parents at Nazareth* (Guildhall Art Gallery, London) exhibited in 1847, prefigures the theme and to a certain extent the style of Millais's *Christ in the House of His Parents* (Tate Gallery) begun in 1849.

Herbert became a master in the Government Schools of Design under the directorship of William Dyce (q.v.) in 1841. He subsequently received a number of fresco commissions for the new Houses of Parliament (see Appendix II). He was elected an Associate of the Royal Academy in 1841 and an Academician in 1846. From 1830 to 1889 (the year before his death in London, March, 17, 1890), he exhibited a total of one hundred and two works at the Academy.

Bibliography

Richard Redgrave and Samuel Redgrave, *A Century of Painters of the English School,* London, 1883, pp. 465-467, (2nd edition).
Christopher Wood, *The Dictionary of Victorian Painters,* London, 1971, p. 64.

24. * THE MONASTERY IN THE 14TH CENTURY: BOAR-HUNTERS REFRESHED AT ST. AUGUSTINE'S MONASTERY, CANTERBURY

Oil on canvas: 54-3/4 x 82 inches
Inscribed, lower left: *J. R. Herbert: R.A.,*
middle center: *Ave Maria Gratia Plena*
Original slip frame

The Monastery in the 14th Century was painted about the time Herbert was converted to Catholicism (c. 1840), and it is a transitional work in many ways. Although painted for the most part in the broad, loose manner of his early, more romantic style, there are suggestions of the tighter, brighter, almost Nazarene style of his later works, especially in the brilliant coloring and firmer outlines of the mounted huntress. Had the artist not been seriously ill prior to the opening of the Academy exhibition, the picture might have been more fully worked in this manner. It is Herbert's first exhibited painting with a religious theme and, in light of his conversion, almost a symbolic one. Like the boar-hunters being received and refreshed by the monks, he was taken in by the Catholic Church and given Holy Communion.

Critical reaction to the picture was favorable. The reviewer of the *Art Union* enthused:

> A finer composition than this does not grace the walls of the Exhibition; and, in parts, the execution is on a par with the conception. . . . The picture will interest all who examine it. . . . The arrangements are skillful and judicious, and minor portions evidence thought and care.

William Makepeace Thackeray in his criticism of the exhibition which first appeared under the pseudonym of Michael Angelo Titmarsh in *Fraser's Magazine* was less lavish in his praise, but nonetheless, favorably impressed.

> If Mr. Herbert's picture of 'Travellers Refreshing at a Convent Gate' has not produced much sensation, it is because it is feeble in tone, not very striking in subject, and placed somewhat too high. There is a great deal of beauty and delicacy in all the figures; and though lost here, amidst the glare and bustle of the Academy, will be an excellent picture for the cabinet, where its quiet graces and merits will be better seen.

During the next five decades Herbert devoted himself almost exclusively to religious subjects. However, this painting does not depict a traditional religious subject drawn from a Biblical source. As in several subsequent pictures by Herbert, the subject is based upon the history of the Catholic Church as it had once existed in the British Isles. The setting is the monastery founded by St. Augustine at Canterbury in the sixth century. Through much of the Middle Ages it was the burial place of kings and archbishops, the holiest religious shrine in England, and the second most important Benedictine house in Europe. In 1844 a college for training missionaries was established on the site. Herbert's picture may have been inspired by Edwin Landseer's *Scene in the Olden Time at Bolton Abbey,* which had been exhibited at the Royal Academy in 1834 and was one of Landseer's most admired works, but for Herbert the subject of a medieval monastery would have had special significance. In 1836 his mentor and friend, A. W. N. Pugin, had published *Contrasts: or a Parallel between the Noble Edifices of the Middle Ages and the corresponding Buildings of the Present Day; showing the Present Decay of Taste.* This book contrasted in plate after plate the ugliness and the soullessness of nineteenth-century England to the good life of the Middle Ages, grounded in Roman Catholicism. Like the plates in *Contrasts,* Herbert's picture depicts an idealized vision of a pre-Reformation England in which the Catholic Church provided both spiritual and material sustenance. This vision was not only a concomitant of Pugin's and Herbert's conversions, but also, in their works, effective propaganda for the re-establishment of a Roman Catholic hierarchy in England, which came to pass with the "papal aggression" of 1850, a decade after Herbert's picture was exhibited.

The signature, or at least the "R.A." of the signature, must be a later addition, since Herbert did not become a full member of the Royal Academy until six full years after this picture was exhibited. In large passages of the picture the pigment was mixed with bitumen, which inevitably leads to the deterioration of the paint surface. As Herbert did not die until 1890, it is possible that he may have had to restore the picture himself at which time the could have added the "R.A."

Provenance

S. Berkeley Owen, Bickleigh Castle, Devon (Sale: Sotheby's, London, May 20, 1970, Lot 76).

Exhibitions

Royal Academy, 1840, No. 287.
The Art and Mind of Victorian England: Paintings from the Forbes Magazine Collection, University Gallery, University of Minnesota, Minneapolis, 1974, No. 18 (reproduced in catalogue).

References

Art Union, 1840, pp. 75-76.
[William Makepeace Thackeray], "A Pictorial Rhapsody by Michael Angelo Titmarsh with an introductory letter to Mr. Yorke," *Fraser's Magazine,* June, 1840 (reprinted in *The Paris Sketchbook and Art Criticisms,* The Oxford Thackeray, Vol. II, p. 523).

24. J. R. Herbert, *The Monastery in the 14th Century;*
Boar-Hunters Refreshed at
St. Augustine's Monastery, Canterbury.
(*see color Plate VIII, p. 166*)

SIR HUBERT VON HERKOMER, RA
(1849-1914)

not only painted pictures but also wrote music and operas, acted, designed stage scenery and even lived long enough to create some movie sets. He was born on May 26, 1849 in Waal, Bavaria, the son of a wood-carver and engraver from whom he received his first training. In 1857, the family moved to England and settled in Southampton. Herkomer entered the South Kensington Schools in 1866. He also studied in Munich, and he returned frequently to Germany throughout his life. His first great success was *The Last Muster—Sunday at the Royal Hospital, Chelsea* (Lady Lever Art Gallery, Port Sunlight), which he exhibited at the Royal Academy in 1875. The subject of this picture depended upon *The Harbour of Refuge* (Tate Gallery), exhibited in 1872 by Frederick Walker (1840-1875), an artist whose important influence Herkomer readily acknowledged. Herkomer was primarily a painter of genre subjects, but he also painted landscapes and was a very successful portraitist. His subjects included Wagner, Ruskin, Lord Kitchener and the German Imperial family. He also made a large group portrait of *The Firm of Friedrich Krupp* shortly before his death on March 31, 1914. He became an Associate of the Royal Academy in 1879, and an Academician in 1890. During his long career he exhibited two hundred and ten works there. In 1883 he founded a School of Art at Bushey in Hertfordshore, and in 1885 he was named Slade Professor of Fine Arts at Oxford. Among other honors conferred upon him were the Legion of Honor, 1880; Membership in the Royal Watercolor Society, 1894; CVO, 1900; and knighthood, 1907. In 1889 he was also elevated to noble rank by the Kaiser. This entitled him to add the prefix "von" to his name. Von Herkomer was fortunate never to have to choose between his loyalties to Britain and Germany. World War I did not break out until several months *after* his death.

Bibliography

Wilfrid Meynell, "Hubert Herkomer, ARA," *The Magazine of Art*, Vol. III, 1880, pp. 259-263.

W. L. Courtney, "Professor Hubert Herkomer, His Life and Work," *Art Annual: Supplement to the Art Journal*, 1892.

Ludwig Pietsch, *Herkomer*, Leipzig, 1901.

Alfred L. Baldry, *Hubert von Herkomer, CVO, RA, A Study and a Biography*, London, 1901.

Sir Hubert von Herkomer, *My School and My Gospel*, London, 1908.

Sir Hubert von Herkomer, *The Herkomers*, London, 1910.

J. Saxon Mills, *Life and Letters of Sir Hubert Herkomer, A Study in Struggle and Success*, London, 1923.

25. * THE FIRST-BORN

Oil on canvas: 44 x 56 inches
Inscribed, lower right: *H.H. '87*
Original frame

Herkomer exhibited eight works at the Royal Academy in 1887: six portraits, one engraving, and *The First-Born*, his only important subject picture of the year. By the mid-1880s Herkomer had become established as a portraitist, and his efforts were concentrated in that most lucrative field of endeavor.

The *Magazine of Art* passed over *The First-Born* completely, but the reviewer for the *Art Journal* commented that it was a painting "in which both landscape and figures are equally good." The picture is painted in free manner with impasto used to a limited extent in the sky. The broad sweep of the road echoes the composition of Herkomer's *Hard Times* (City Art Gallery, Manchester), which he had exhibited at the Royal Academy two years before, but unlike that picture, whose title is indicative of its somber content, *The First-Born* is a scene of idyllic village life. Like many of Herkomer's pictures it echoes the earlier treatment of similar themes by Frederick Walker (1840-1875). It may also owe some inspiration to *The Village Wedding* by Luke Fildes (q.v.), exhibited at the Royal Academy in 1885, but Fildes also followed Walker's lead in painting lyrical scenes of idealized rural life.

Provenance

Anon. Sale: Sotheby's, London, May 20, 1970, Lot 64.

Exhibitions

Royal Academy, 1887, No. 647.

The Art and Mind of Victorian England: Paintings from the Forbes Magazine Collection, University Gallery, University of Minnesota, Minneapolis, 1974, No. 19 (reproduced in catalogue).

References

Art Journal, 1887, p. 278.

The Illustrated London News, May 28, 1887, p. 608.

Alfred L. Baldry, *Hubert von Herkomer, CVO, RA, A Study and a Biography*, London, 1901, p. 34.

J. Saxon Mills, *Life and Letters of Sir Hubert Herkomer, A Study in Struggle and Success*, London, 1923, p. 172.

Michael A. Findlay, "Forbes Saves the Queen," *Arts Magazine*, February, 1973, p. 30, reproduced p. 26.

Melvin Waldfogel, "Introduction," *The Art and Mind of Victorian England: Paintings from the Forbes Magazine Collection*, University Gallery, University of Minnesota, Minneapolis, 1974, pp. 19, 22 (exhibition catalogue).

Lyndel King, "Heroism began at home," *Art News*, November, 1974, p. 45.

H. von Herkomer, *Hard Times*
(City Art Gallery, Manchester)

25. H. von Herkomer, *The First-Born.*
(*see color Plate IX, p. 167*)

JOHN EVAN HODGSON, RA
(1831-1895)

was born in London in 1831. While he was still a young child, his family moved to Russia where his father was engaged in what Clement and Hutton refer to as "mercantile pursuits." He returned to England to attend school at Rugby and then after a brief attempt at a commercial career in London, he entered the Royal Academy Schools in 1853. He made his debut at the Academy's annual Summer Exhibition three years later with a work entitled *The Notice of Ejectment*. His next exhibited works alternated between depictions of events from English history and contemporary genre subjects. After a trip to North Africa in 1868, Hodgson dwelt almost exclusively on Eastern subjects. He was a member of the St. John's Wood Clique (see Appendix I) and his house at 5 Hill Road, St. John's Wood, was one of the group's favorite gathering places. At their rendezvous Hodgson often entertained his guests with bogus Scottish sermons. Hodgson found an appreciative audience for both his pre- and post-Eastern works, and in 1872 he was elected an Associate of the Royal Academy. He became a full Academician seven years later. In 1882 he was made the Librarian of the Academy as well as the Professor of Painting. Before his death on June 19, 1895, he exhibited some ninety paintings at that institution and with Sir Frederick A. Eaton, the Secretary of the Academy, he was co-author of *The Royal Academy and Its Members, 1768-1830*, published in 1905.

Bibliography

Clara Clement and Lawrence Hutton, *Artists of the Nineteenth Century*, London, 1879, pp. 359-360.
Art Journal, 1895, p. 256, (obituary).
Bevis Hillier, "The St. John's Wood Clique," *Apollo*, June, 1964, pp. 490-495.

26. * "THE QUEEN, GOD BLESS HER!"

Oil on panel, arched top: 26 x 36 inches
Inscribed, lower right: *J. E. Hodgson 80*
Original slip frame

"*The Queen, God Bless Her!*" received no notice in the press reviews of the Royal Academy exhibition of 1885. The scene depicted is two soldiers in the desert toasting their monarch. The pyramids, symbols of the greatest civilization of the Pre-Classical world, are visible on the horizon. The two soldiers are the representatives of a new civilization and a New Empire, that of Queen Victoria's England. At a time when European powers were scrambling to carve out spheres of influences in the Pacific, the Near East and Africa, this picture seems to provide an amusing commentary on Britain's calm assertion of supremacy in Egypt. However, in the spring of 1885, when this painting was exhibited, its subject would certainly have reminded visitors to the Royal Academy of the expeditionary army which had traveled up the Nile in an unsuccessful attempt to save General Gordon. The news of the fall of Khartoum and of Gordon's death reached London on February 5, 1885, producing public hysteria and an outcry against the government. Under the circumstances, the relaxed attitudes of the two soldiers might be interpreted as a critical comment on the unhurried pace with which the army had carried out its mission.

Provenance

Anon. Sale: Phillip's, London, June 22, 1970, Lot P.197.

Exhibitions

Royal Academy, 1885, No. 265.
The Art and Mind of Victorian England: Paintings from the Forbes Magazine Collection, University Gallery, University of Minnesota, Minneapolis, 1974, No. 20 (reproduced in catalogue).

References

Michael A. Findlay, "Forbes Saves the Queen," *Arts Magazine*, February, 1973, p. 30, reproduced p. 29.
Melvin Waldfogel, "Introduction," *The Art and Mind of Victorian England: Paintings from the Forbes Magazine Collection*, University Gallery, University of Minnesota, Minneapolis, 1974, p. 22 (exhibition catalogue).
"A glimpse of Victoria's world," *Minneapolis Tribune*, September 22, 1974, reproduced.

26. J. E. Hodgson, *"The Queen, God Bless Her!"*

FRANK HOLL, RA
(1845-1888)

was born in London in 1845, the son of the engraver Francis Holl (1815-1884). He entered the Royal Academy Schools first as a probationer and then as a student in 1860. Two years later he won a Silver Medal for "the best drawing from the antique" and the following year, he won a Gold Medal "for the best historical painting," and another Silver Medal for "the second-best drawing from the life." In 1864 he made his first appearance as an exhibitor at the Royal Academy with two pictures: *A Portrait* and *Turned Out of Church.* Portraiture and dramatic social realism were to remain the hallmarks of Holl's *oeuvre* throughout his brief career. In 1869 *The Lord Gave, and the Lord Hath Taken Away; Blessed Be the Name of the Lord* won for Holl a two-year traveling scholarship, a part of which he spent in Italy. Upon his return, he received a commission from Queen Victoria. The result, *No Tidings from the Sea,* was exhibited at the Royal Academy in 1871. Seven years later, his *Newgate—Committed for Trial* caused a small sensation when it appeared at the Academy, echoing the success of *Applicants for Admission to a Casual Ward* by Luke Fildes (q.v.). Holl's frequently gloomy pictures caused the critic James Dafforne to query: "Will Mr. Holl allow me to suggest to him a trial of the sunny side of human nature?" Holl did not take Dafforne's suggestion. He did, however, concentrate increasingly on portraiture and from 1885 until his death in 1888, he exhibited only portraits at the Academy.

Holl was elected an Associate Academician in 1878 and a full Member in 1883. That same year his father was elected an Associate Academician. In 1888 he fell ill on a trip to Spain, and he died several months later at the age of forty-three, after literally rising from his deathbed at the behest of J. P. Morgan, who had traveled from America expressly to sit for the portrait which now hangs in the Morgan Library in New York. Holl's contemporaries believed that his enormous success as a portaitist had led him to kill himself by overwork. He exhibited eighty-seven works at the Royal Academy during his short life.

Bibliography

James Dafforne, "The Works of Frank Holl," *Art Journal,* 1876, pp. 9-12.

Wilfred Meynell, "Frank Holl, RA," in *Some Modern Artists and Their Work,* ed. Wilfred Meynell, London, 1883, pp. 166-173.

Gertrude E. Campbell, "Frank Holl and His Works," *Art Journal,* 1889, pp. 85-91.

A. M. Reynolds, *The Life and Works of Frank Holl,* London, 1912.

27. * HER FIRST BORN

Oil on board: 13-3/4 x 19-3/4 inches
Inscribed, lower right: *Frank Holl 1877*

Her First Born is a reduced replica of the picture of the same title exhibited at the Royal Academy in 1876 (Dundee City Art Gallery). It is typical of the tragic or pathetic subjects painted by Holl prior to turning almost exclusively to portraiture. The death of children was a more common occurrence a hundred years ago than today, especially among the urban and rural poor. Unlike the impassive realism of a work like Courbet's *Burial at Ornans* of 1849 (Louvre, Paris), *Her First Born* represents an overt attempt to rend the viewer's heart. The picture is the complete opposite in feeling to *The First-Born* by Hubert von Herkomer (see No. 25) exhibited in 1887. In one, the pride of the humble parents is as palpable as the sorrow of their counterparts in the other. In both, their creators practiced what Herkomer claimed to have learned in England: "that truth in art must be enhanced by sentiment."

When *Her First Born* appeared at the Royal Academy, the reviewer for *The Illustrated London News* was restrained in his reaction: "We come again upon incidents of country life of sad complexion. . . . The colouring partakes of the mournfulness of the theme" (May 13, 1876, p. 475). The critic for the *Art Journal,* on the other hand, declared: "Mr. Holl, we are sure, never painted better or made the onlooker sadder" (1876, p. 261). Before drawing this conclusion, the same writer proposed that "for matters melancholy F. Holl is unquestionably *facile princeps.* His sway this year may be disputed by Mr. Fildes [who exhibited *The Wid-ower*], but Mr. Holl is preeminently the man who preaches to us with perennial impressiveness that—

'Life is real, life is earnest,
And the grave is not its goal;
Dust thou art, to dust returnest,
Was not spoken of the soul.' "

According to the artist's daughter, the background of *Her First Born* was based on the quaint old churchyard at Shere in Surrey. This small replica, executed the year after the large picture was exhibited, was painted for the artist's family, in whose possession it remained until recently.

Provenance

Mrs. E. M. Dartford, Ashley, Shalbourne nr. Marlborough, Wilts, granddaughter of the artist.
Fine Art Society, London.
Anon. Sale: Sotheby's Belgravia, London, June 12, 1973, Lot 138, reproduced.
Fine Art Society, London (Agents).

Exhibitions

Recent Acquisitions, Fine Art Society, London, 1969, No. 50.
The Art and Mind of Victorian England: Paintings from the Forbes Magazine Collection, University Gallery, University of Minnesota, Minneapolis, 1974, No. 21 (reproduced in catalogue).

References

Dundee City Art Gallery Catalogue: The Permanent Collection of Paintings, Drawings and Sculpture, Dundee Corporation, 1973, p. 63.
Melvin Waldfogel, "Introduction", *The Art and Mind of Victorian England: Paintings from the Forbes Magazine Collection,* University Gallery, University of Minnesota, Minneapolis, 1974, p. 19 (exhibition catalogue).
Lyndel King, "Heroism began at home," *Art News.* November. 1974, p. 45.

F. Holl, *Her First Born*
(Dundee City Art Gallery, Scotland)

27. F. Holl, *Her First Born.*

JOHN CALLCOTT HORSLEY, RA
(1817-1903)

was the nephew of the prominent landscape painter Sir Augustus Wall Callcott (1779-1844) whom Ruskin described as painting "everything tolerably, nothing excellently." He was also the brother-in-law of the great engineer Isambard Kingdom Brunel.

Horsley was born in London, January 29, 1817 and he studied at the Royal Academy Schools. He first exhibited at the Royal Academy in 1839, and in the 1840s he made a reputation as a history painter. In 1843 he participated in the competitions to select artists to paint frescoes in the new Houses of Parliament (see Appendix II), and in 1845 he did receive a commission to execute a fresco of *The Spirit of Religion* in the House of Lords.

In the 1850s he turned to contemporary genre subjects and only returned to historical subjects to provide period settings for lighthearted *tableaux.* In 1866 he settled at Sittinghurst in Kent, where he became associated with the nearby Cranbrook Colony (see Appendix I), although he did not paint many pictures of children of the type specialized in by Thomas Webster (q.v.) and his fellow Cranbrook artists. Horsley's best-known later works are pictures of attractive young lovers. His constant, prudish objections to the use of nude models, earned him the epithet "Clothes Horsley" as well as Whistler's remark, *"Horsley soit qui mal y pense."* Horsley was elected an Associate member of the Royal Academy in 1855 and a full Member in 1864. He organized the first Old Master Winter Exhibitions at the Academy after the British Institution closed in 1867, and from 1882 to 1897 he was the Academy's Treasurer. Between 1830 and 1897, when he retired from membership, he exhibited one hundred and twenty-one works at the Academy.

Bibliography
"British Artists: Their Style and Character; No. XXV—John Calcott Horsley, ARA," *Art Journal,* 1857, pp. 181-184.
John Calcott Horsley, *Recollections of a Royal Academician,* London, 1903.

the latter picture is not known. The former work, is a costume piece reminiscent of the "Keepsake" beauties of C. R. Leslie (q.v.), Maclise (q.v.), Frith (q.v.), and Egg (q.v.). These were idealized portraits of pretty young women and were called "Keepsake" pictures because the type was popularized by engraved illustrations in annual gift-book publications, of which one of the best-known was entitled *The Keepsake.* Neither *Madame Se Chauffe* nor its pendant was noticed by the contemporary press as they were overshadowed by Horsley's major Academy contribution of 1871, an historical picture of *Mary Queen of Scots in Captivity.* Horsley makes no mention of the pair in his memoirs, *Recollections of a Royal Academician.*

Madame Se Chauffe is typical of Horsley's later *oeuvre.* Without the picture of *Monsieur* one cannot say definitely, but it is reasonable to suppose that the letter clasped in Madame's hand is as important to her warmth as the fire before which she stands. A smaller (6 x 4 inches) pair of replicas from the collection of Stephen G. Holland were sold at Christie's, London, on June 25, 1908, Lot 59 for £14 14s.

Provenance
Anon. Sale: Sotheby's, London, February 17, 1971, Lot 51.
Thomas Agnew & Sons, London (Agents).

Exhibitions
Royal Academy, 1871, No. 527.
The Art and Mind of Victorian England: Paintings from the Forbes Magazine Collection, University Gallery, University of Minnesota, Minneapolis, 1974, No. 22 (reproduced in catalogue).

References
"Morals at the Academy," *Punch,* May 13, 1871, p. 196.

28. *MADAME SE CHAUFFE

Oil on panel: 21 x 14-1/4 inches
Inscribed, lower right: *J. C. Horsley. 1871*
Original frame

Madame Se Chauffe was exhibited at the Royal Academy in 1871 with a pendant entitled *Monsieur Se Chauffe.* The present location of

28. J. C. Horsley, *Madame Se Chauffe*.

CHARLES HUNT

(1803-1877)

was a minor painter of humorous genre scenes, usually involving children. Graham Reynolds in *Victorian Painters,* classifies him among those "almost unknown artists . . . [who] attain a standard of achievement which ensures their continuing interest."

He was born in 1803 and is recorded as exhibiting in London as early as 1846, although his work did not appear at the Royal Academy's Summer Exhibition until 1862. His entry of that year, a work entitled *Vocal and Instrumental* was listed by the reviewer of the *Art Journal* among those works which "belong to a class that frequently escape observation from being hung necessarily low." His next entry was a picture depicting a children's parody of the play scene in *Hamlet* ("The Play's the thing, wherein I'll catch the conscience of the King," *Hamlet,* Act ii. sc. 2). This work was described in the *Art Journal* as a "good example of the Webster School." Thomas Webster (q.v.) and a group of artists who settled near him at Cranbrook in Kent (see Appendix I) specialized in humorous pictures of children. Whether Hunt had any direct relationship with the members of the Cranbrook Colony is uncertain, but their influence on his work is evident. Hunt found his *Hamlet* successful enough to mix Shakespeare and children again in 1864 with *The Banquet Scene, 'Macbeth'* which received favorable reviews, and again in 1868 with *The Trial Scene, 'Merchant of Venice'.* Before his death on November 15, 1877, he showed nine works at the Royal Academy and several more at the British Institution and the Society of British Artists.

Bibliography

Christopher Wood, *The Dictionary of Victorian Painters,* London, 1971, p. 72.

29. MY 'MACBETH'

Oil on canvas: 20 x 26 inches
Inscribed, middle right: *C. HUNT 1863;*
lower right: *C. HUNT 1863*

My 'Macbeth' was never exhibited at the Royal Academy. It is an autobiographical work comprising a self-portrait of the artist with his wife and son, set in a comfortable, cluttered Victorian interior. He is in the act of pointing out to them one of his favorite paintings, which was also one of his most successful Royal Academy pictures. The painting toward which Hunt ges-

tures is *The Banquet Scene, 'Macbeth',* which he exhibited at the Academy in 1864. When it was exhibited, the *Art Journal* described Hunt as "another of our artists who strive to make, as it were, the gallery audience of the Academy ring with peals of laughter." The painting was treated with an equally generous description:

> A boy ghost, robed in white sheets, points the finger of avenging destiny towards the guilty Macbeth. The lady of this mock tragedy bids, in mien of due solemnity, her guests begone. Yet boys stil! there are at the banquet, who will persist in eating the good things set before them. The tale is capitally told, and the picture equally well painted.

In *My 'Macbeth',* a copy of the *Art Journal* lies prominently on the chair next to the easel. If the painting was executed in 1863 as it is dated, then it is likely that the magazine was painted in after the glowing review of *The Banquet Scene, 'Macbeth'* appeared in it in 1864. This would be in keeping with the "daring supra-reality and the lack of self-consciousness" that Mario Amaya saw in the painting when it was exhibited in London almost one hundred years later. Or, as Anthony Powell, wrote in the *Daily Telegraph,* "That mysterious picture *My 'Macbeth'*. . . might almost be School of Magritte."

Provenance

M. Newman Ltd., London
Berry-Hill Galleries, Inc., New York

Exhibitions

The Victorian Scene, M. Newman Ltd., London, 1962.
The Art and Mind of Victorian England: Paintings from the Forbes Magazine Collection, University Gallery, University of Minnesota, Minneapolis, 1974, No. 23 (reproduced in catalogue).

References

Mario Amaya, "Nineteenth Century Art: The Opening Vista," *Apollo,* December, 1962, p. 807.
Anthony Powell, "Best Bad Painters in the World," *Daily Telegraph,* February 3, 1972.
Melvin Waldfogel, "Introduction," *The Art and Mind of Victorian England: Paintings from the Forbes Magazine Collection,* University Gallery, University of Minnesota, Minneapolis, 1974, p. 19 (exhibition catalogue).
Carole Nelson, "Exhibition Wins Respect for Long Neglected Victorian Paintings," *St. Paul's Sunday Pioneer Press, Family Life Section,* September 29, 1974, reproduced in color p. 1.

29. C. Hunt, *My 'Macbeth'*.

WILLIAM HOLMAN HUNT,
(1827-1910)

was born on Wood Street, Cheapside on April 2, 1827. He was the eldest of the seven children of William Hunt, a warehouse manager, who survived to maturity. His parents were willing to allow him to indulge in art on an amateur basis but were very much opposed to his taking it up as a profession. As a result he spent his early teens as a clerk in various offices. During this period, however, he met and was encouraged by John Varley (1778-1842) and took painting lessons from Henry Rogers, a minor portrait painter. Finally, in 1843, after a portrait he executed attracted some favorable attention, Hunt received his father's consent to take up painting professionally. In 1844 he was accepted as a probationer at the Royal Academy Schools; he became a full student in January of the following year. While a probationer, he met John Everett Millais (q.v.). Four years later he and Millais and another fellow student, Dante Gabriel Rossetti (1828-1832), formed the Pre-Raphaelite Brotherhood (see Appendix I). Prior to this, Hunt had begun to experiment with painting over a white ground. The brilliant colors that resulted from this method became one of the hallmarks of early Pre-Raphaelite paintings. In 1849 Hunt made his first trip to the Continent, with Rossetti, and four years later, on January 16, 1854, he departed for the Holy Land. He did not return to England until 1856. That year he submitted his name as a candidate for Associate membership of the Academy, but was rejected. Hunt exhibited a total of twenty-five works at the Academy, but he sent the majority of them in the decade from 1846 to 1856. He did not exhibit there at all after 1874, and from 1860 onwards he relied on dealers and private exhibitions to show and sell his work. In later years he achieved a great reputation from pictures of religious subjects, for which he made several additional trips to the East, and which he sold for phenomenally high prices. In 1905 he was awarded the Order of Merit by King Edward VII.

Among the original members of the Pre-Raphaelite Brotherhood, only Hunt's style remained virtually unchanged after the early 1850s. He never considered the later works of Rossetti or those of Burne-Jones as being Pre-Raphaelite, and he continued to paint with moral fervor and precise detail until his death in 1910.

Bibliography

Alice Meynell and Archdeacon Farrar, D.D., "William Holman Hunt: His Life and Works," *Art Annual: Supplement to the Art Journal*, 1893.
William Holman Hunt, *Pre-Raphaelitism and the Pre-Raphaelite Brotherhood*, 2 Vols., London, 1905.
A. C. Gissing, *William Holman Hunt: A Biography*, London, 1936.
Mary Bennet, *William Holman Hunt*, Walker Art Gallery, Liverpool, 1969 (exhibition catalogue).

30. * II DOLCE FAR NIENTE

Oil on canvas: 39 x 32-1/2 inches
Inscribed, lower left: *WHH* (monogram) *1866*
Original frame

In his memoirs Hunt places the commencement of this picture in 1860 and gives a succinct account of its history:

> Having long been engaged on works of scale below life-size, it seemed wise now to take up the painting of figures of full proportions. Through the kindness of friends a young lady sat to me, and I commenced a picture which I afterwards called "II dolce far niente." I made use of the Egyptian chairs, which, having been borrowed and painted by other artists, were no longer attractive to me for Oriental subjects. I was glad of the opportunity of exercising myself in work which had not any didactic purpose. The picture, however, had to be laid by for the time, and finished at a later period from another model.

He took it up again in 1865, completed it in 1866, and exhibited it at the Royal Academy in 1867, at which time the reviewer for the *Art Journal* classified it as "a picture of costume" and complained that the picture "cannot be commended even for its beauty."

The "Egyptian chairs" which Hunt mentions were designed by him in 1857 and are now in the City Art Gallery, Birmingham. The "young lady" from whom he began the picture was his quondam protégée and fiancée Annie Miller. Their tortured relationship (which is described by Diana Holman Hunt in *My Grandfather: His Wives and Loves*) ceased because Annie, who had been a professional model, refused to sever her connections with other men. She was the cause of a break between Hunt and Dante Gabriel Rossetti (1828-1882) in 1857 and was the model for Rossetti's *Helen of Troy* of 1863 (Kunsthalle, Hamburg), where the hair is recognizably the same as in Hunt's pictures. Apparently Hunt had not finished the face before his final split with Annie, and when he recommenced the picture he completed it from the features of Fanny Waugh, whom he married in December 1865. In the words of Diana Holman Hunt: "The relaxed pose of a professional and the clothes are typical of Annie. Fanny's strong yet sensuous features, without the long straight hair she had, make the total effect so incongruous that the model looks like a female impersonator in drag." Fanny died in December

1866, after giving birth to a son. In 1866 Hunt began a more conventional portrait of her, which he completed after her death. In 1875 he married her younger sister.

Diana Holman Hunt, who ascribes the commencement of the picture to 1859, states that its title stems from that time and is a teasing reference to Annie Miller's indolence. However, Hunt wrote in the passage quoted above that he "afterwards" called it "II dolce far niente," and a letter written by William Michael Rossetti to Hunt in December 1865 (John Rylands Library, Manchester), which translates the phrase ("the sweet doing nothing"), suggests that Hunt only assigned the title to the picture as he was completing it. According to Hunt, the work "had not any didactic purpose." It was begun as a formal exercise and as a fanciful portrait of someone to whom he was close.

The figure is illuminated by two sources of light: a window to our right, and a fire before which she is seated; both the window and the fireplace are visible in the mirror in the background. At least two Pre-Raphaelite pictures of the previous decade, *An English Fireside* of 1854-5 by Ford Madox Brown (1821-1893) and *Faces in the Fire* by John Brett (q.v.), were studies of figures illuminated by firelight. Mirrors appear in the backgrounds of several earlier Pre-Raphaelite pictures, including Hunt's *Awakening Conscience* of 1853; the inspiration seems to have come from the mirror in the background of the *Arnolfini Marriage* by Jan Van Eyck, which had entered the National Gallery in London in 1842. An elaborate sequence of mirrors appears in the background of Hunt's portrait of Fanny begun in 1866.

In subject *II Dolce Far Niente* is similar to Rossetti's fanciful portraits of women which he began to paint in 1859, and Hunt's title recalls the Italian titles of many of Rossetti's pictures. Although Hunt and Rossetti were no longer friends, it is comprehensible that in painting the person who caused their quarrel Hunt, perhaps unconsciously, fell into a Rossettian vein. A watercolor begun in 1860 by Rossetti of *Lucretia Borgia* (Tate Gallery) has a similar round mirror in a similar position in the background. Rossetti's watercolor is closely related to a watercolor from the same year by Edward Burne-Jones (1833-1898) of *Sidonia von Bork* (Tate Gallery) which, as John Christian has pointed out (*Burlington Magazine*, CXV, 1973, p. 106), was directly influenced by Giulio Romano's *Portrait of Isabella d'Este* at Hampton Court Palace. The abrupt transition from the scale of the foreground figure to the reflection in the mirror and the lines of the sumptuous

30. W. H. Hunt, *Il Dolce Far Niente*.
(*see color Plate X, p. 168*)

dress in *Il Dolce Far Niente* may also have been inspired by the *Portrait of Isabella d'Este*, which Hunt could easily have known from visits to Hampton Court. This was Hunt's first ambitious painting of a life-sized figure. His interest in working on a larger scale paralleled developments in the art of both Rossetti and Millais at about the same time, and for prototypes all three artists began to look away from the fifteenth-century sources of earlier Pre-Raphaelitism to the richer art of the following centuries.

Provenance

Pocock Collection
N. N. Lewis
Hiram Craven, The Biery, Sunderland (Sale: Christie's, London, March 21, 1896, Lot 283).
Thomas S. Brocklebank, Wateringbury Place, Kent (Sale: Christie's, London, July 8, 1938, Lot 16, £ 241 10s).
Mrs. Michael Joseph, daughter of the artist.
Mrs. Michael Burt, by descent (Sale: Christie's, London, March 17, 1961, Lot 68).
John Richardson, New York
Mr. and Mrs. Robert Walker, London

Exhibitions

Royal Academy, 1867, No. 678.
Liverpool Autumn Exhibition, 1875, No. 311.
City Art Gallery, Manchester, 1906, No. 59.
Walker Art Gallery, Liverpool, 1907, No. 24.
Bournemouth, 1951, No. 28.
The Pre-Raphaelites, Herron Museum of Art, Indianapolis and Gallery of Modern Art, New York, 1964, No 46 (reproduced in catalogue).
Artists of Victoria's England, Cummer Gallery of Art, Jacksonville, Florida, 1965, No. 30 (reproduced in catalogue).
European and American Art from Princeton Alumni Collections, The Art Museum, Princeton University, Princeton, 1972, No. 49 (reproduced in catalogue).

References

Art Journal, 1867, p. 143.
"Art Notes," *The Reader*, December 16, 1865, p. 692.
[J. Beavington Atkinson], "The Royal Academy and other Exhibitions," *Blackwood's*, Vol. 102, 1867, p. 89.
The Illustrated London News, May 25, 1867, p. 519.
William Holman Hunt, *Pre-Raphaelitism and the Pre-Raphaelite Brotherhood*, London, 1905-1906, Vol. II, p. 203, reproduced p. 204.
Otto Wilhelm von Schleinitz, *William H. Hunt*, Bielefeld und Leipzig, 1907, p. 75, reproduced p. 76.
Stuart Preston, "Pre-Raphaelites in New York," *Apollo*, June, 1964, pp. 512-513, reproduced p. 513.
Diana Holman Hunt, *My Grandfather: His Wives and Loves*, London, 1969, pp. 202-203, 237, 245.
Marina Varzey, "The Robert Walker Collection, Part I," *Connoisseur*, September, 1971, pp. 16-17, reproduced p. 16.
Thomas L. Sloan, "Nineteenth Century French and English Painters," *European and American Art from Princeton Alumni Collections*, The Art Museum, Princeton University, Princeton, 1972, p. 59 (exhibition catalogue).

Michael Findlay, "Forbes Saves the Queen," *Arts Magazine*, February, 1973, p. 27, reproduced p. 28.

Forthcoming References

George Landow, *William Holman Hunt, typology, and Early Pre-Raphaelite Symbolism*, Yale University Press, 1976.

31. HOUNDS

Oil on board: 9-3/4 x 11-1/2 inches
Original frame

This small panel contains studies for the pictures which Hunt exhibited at the Royal Academy in 1847 and 1848. The standing hound is repeated almost exactly in the earlier of the two, *Dr. Rochecliffe Performing Divine Service in the Cottage of Joceline Joliffe at Woodstock*, based on Sir Walter Scott's novel *Woodstock*. The hounds also appear in a preliminary study for the picture Hunt exhibited in the following year, *The Flight of Madeline and Porphyro During the Drunkenness Attending the Revelry*, based upon John Keats's poem "The Eve of St. Agnes." The final version of *The Flight of Madeline and Porphyro* (Guildhall Art Gallery, London) includes the sleeping hound painted in outline in the upper left corner of this sketch, but facing in the opposite direction. In the extended quotation from Scott which Hunt included in the Royal Academy catalogue in 1847 there is no mention of hounds, but the quotation from "The Eve of St. Agnes" which accompanied *The Flight of Madeline and Porphyro* includes the following lines,

'The wakeful bloodhound rose, and shook
   his hide,
But his sagacious eye an inmate owns;'

W. H. Hunt, *Woodstock* — detail
(Private Collection)

and the hounds play a role in the narrative as observers who do not hinder the fleeing lovers.

The actual bloodhound used as the model for these sketches was lent to Hunt by a friend, J. Blount Price. Although in Hunt's pictures of the 1840s the hounds play only subordinate roles, in the following decade two of his most important pictures — *Strayed Sheep* (Tate Gallery), exhibited at the Royal Academy in 1853, and *The Scapegoat* (Lady Lever Art Gallery, Port Sunlight), exhibited three years later — were of animal subjects. The attention to the psychological expression of animals in this study suggests the influence of Edwin Landseer (q.v.), an influence which is also evident in Hunt's later animal paintings. However, here we already see Hunt's scrupulous attention to form replacing the virtuoso brilliance of Landseer's surfaces and anticipating the carefully studied detail of Hunt's subsequent Pre-Raphaelite pictures.

On the verso are several figure studies in pencil.

Provenance

M. Price, 24 Milner Square, Islington
P. & D. Colnaghi & Co., Ltd., London

Exhibitions

English Paintings, Drawings and Prints, P. & D. Colhaghi & Co., Ltd., London, 1971, No. 116 (reproduced in catalogue, plate XXXI).
The Art and Mind of Victorian England: Paintings from the Forbes Magazine Collection, University Gallery, University of Minnesota, Minneapolis, 1974, No. 24 (reproduced in catalogue).

References

Michael Findlay, "Forbes Saves the Queen," *Arts Magazine*, February, 1973, p. 30.

W. H. Hunt, *The Flight of Madeline and Porphyro* — detail
(By courtesy of Guildhall Library, City of London)

31. W. H. Hunt, *Hounds*.

CHARLES LANDSEER, RA
(1799-1879)

was one of the seven out of fourteen children of the engraver John Landseer (1769-1852) who survived past adolescence. Charles Landseer's reputation, like that of his older brother, Thomas (1795-1880) an engraver, was very much overshadowed by the success of their exceptionally talented younger brother, Edwin Landseer (q.v.). It was even said that Charles was elected a Royal Academician in 1845 (he had become ARA in 1837) more out of respect and admiration for Edwin than in recognition of his own ability as an artist. W. P. Frith (q.v.) in his *Reminiscences* said of Charles Landseer that he made better puns than pictures. Be that as it may, the older Landseer was a competent painter and some seventy-three of his works, usually historical, literary, or period genre subjects appeared in the Academy's exhibitions from 1828 to 1879.

Landseer studied drawing with his father and painting under the eccentric and occasionally brilliant romantic artist, Benjamin Robert Haydon (1786-1846). Eventually, he entered the Academy schools. In the early 1820s, he was attached to the suite of Sir Stuart de Rothsay and traveled extensively in Portugal and Brazil. Studies and sketches made on this trip were much admired, but he sent to the Academy only one work derived completely from them, *Il Tempo del Carnovale*, exhibited in 1849. Landseer was made Keeper of the Royal Academy in 1851. He resigned the post in 1873 because of his advancing age. When he died six years later, he bequeathed to the Academy the sum of £10,000 to found four scholarships, two in painting and two in sculpture, as well as a set of drawings by George Stubbs (1724-1806) for *The Anatomy of the Horse*, which he had inherited from his younger brother.

Bibliography
Art Journal, 1879, p. 217 (obituary).
Christopher Wood, *The Dictionary of Victorian Painters*, London, 1971, p. 82.

32. THE RETURN OF THE DOVE TO THE ARK

Oil on canvas: 54-1/2 x 73 inches
Original frame

When this picture appeared at the Royal Academy in 1844, it was listed in the catalogue with the following quotation from the Old Testament: "So Noah knew that the waters were abated

from off the earth" (Genesis 8: 11). Unfortunately for Landseer, the deluge of criticism with which the picture was greeted was unabated. The *Art Union* declared,

> It is painful to see labour so ill bestowed as it is in this picture. Of the thousand and one ways of delivering a narrative this artist has taken the driest and most matter-of-fact. Noah and his family are disposed without purpose or effect. . . . In the character of the figures there is nothing that is not hourly before the public eye; they are, in short, drawn as if Noah and his children had been natives of these islands. . . . This is a deplorable evil, but one which is grievously common; the artist often seeming to care nothing whatever for truth; considering prettiness of effect infinitely more 'saleable'. . . . Here then is a lamentable failure— figures made up of models at so much per hour, sitting in the midst of selections from the Surrey Zoological Gardens. . . . A hundred times more imagination than the painter possessed would be necessary before a spectator could conceive himself anywhere but where he is.

In *Fraser's Magazine*, William Makepeace Thackeray was no less severe. In his opinion,

> Brother Charles has sinned. . . . The ark is vulgarized here and reduced to the proportions of a Calais steamer. . . . All the greatness of the subject is lost; . . . they have little more interest than a group of any emigrants in the hold of a ship, who rouse and rally at the sound of 'Land ho!'
>
> Why, if all great themes of poetry are to be treated in this way, the art would be easy. We might have Hector shaving himself before going out to fight Achilles . . . Priam in a cotton nightcap asleep in a four-poster on the night of the sack of Troy, Hecuba, of course, by his side, with curl-papers. . . . No painter has a right to treat great historical subjects in such a fashion.

The critic writing for *The Illustrated London News* was decidedly kinder as well as briefer. After describing the painting as "something too tame," he went on to say, "it has, however, the merit of correct detail, and nothing derogatory to the high rank which the name of Landseer has obtained."

In 1851, John Everett Millais (q.v.) exhibited his own *Return of the Dove to the Ark* (Ashmolean Museum, Oxford). Limited to the two daughters of Noah embracing the returned dove and his olive branch, Millais's simple poignant canvas contrasts dramatically with Landseer's elaborate menagerie. However, in a letter written in January 1851, before he began painting his picture, Millais indicated that he intended to include the figure of Noah praying and a background containing "several birds and animals one of

which now forms the prey of the other." By the time Millais made the beautiful preparatory drawing now in the National Gallery of Canada, he had already reduced the composition to two figures, but as the motif of a girl holding the dove to her breast is essentially the same in Millais's and Landseer's works (and has no Biblical source), it seems likely that Charles Landseer's picture, exhibited while the younger artist was a student in the Royal Academy Schools, provided Millais's initial visual inspiration.

Provenance
Anon. Sale: Sotheby's Belgravia, London, October 19, 1971, Lot 112.
Thomas Agnew & Sons, London (Agents).

Exhibitions
Royal Academy, 1844, No. 287.

References
Art Union, 1844, pp. 159-160.
The Illustrated London News, May 11, 1844, p. 306.
[William Makepeace Thackeray], "May Gambols or, Titmarsh in the Picture galleries," *Fraser's Magazine*, June, 1844 (reprinted in *The Paris Sketchbook and Art Criticisms*, The Oxford Thackeray, Vol. II, pp. 612-614).

J. E. Millais, *The Return of the Dove to the Ark* — drawing (National Gallery of Canada, Ottawa)

32. C. Landseer, *The Return of the Dove to the Ark.*

SIR EDWIN LANDSEER, RA
(1802-1873)

was born in London on March 7, 1802. He was the youngest son of the engraver John Landseer (1769-1852). Two of his brothers were also artists: Charles (q.v.), and Thomas (1795-1880), who, like his father, was an engraver.

Edwin was a child prodigy. After studying with his father and the history painter Benjamin Robert Haydon (1786-1846), he entered the Royal Academy Schools at the age of fourteen. This was two years after he had made his debut at the Academy's annual exhibition with two small paintings, one of dogs and one of a mule. Because of his talent for drawing animals, especially dogs, Henry Fuseli (1741-1825), who was in charge of the drawing classes at the Academy, nicknamed him "my little dog boy." He studied dissection and anatomy and owned George Stubbs's (1724-1806) drawings for *The Anatomy of the Horse*. With John Frederick Lewis (q.v.), three years his junior, he spent hours sketching beasts at the Exeter 'Change. In 1821, the French painter Théodore Géricault (1791-1824) admired his *Rat Catchers* when it was shown at the Academy. Five years later Landseer was elected an Associate of the Royal Academy at the age of twenty-four, the youngest possible age, and in 1831 he was made a full member. In 1834, accompanied by Charles Robert Leslie (q.v.), he made the first of many trips to the Highlands. In later years, he was often the guest of the Royal Family in Scotland, and he was a particular favorite of Queen Victoria from whom he received a large number of commissions including ones for portraits of her dogs (see No. 33) and later her children. Prince Albert also commissioned him to paint one of the frescoes illustrating Milton's *Comus* in the Garden Pavilion at Buckingham Palace (see Appendix II) as well as smaller pictures as birthday presents for his wife.

Besides painting, Landseer also sculpted, and he modelled the lions in Trafalgar Square. During the Victorian period he gained his greatest popularity with his dogs which expressed human sentiments. Landseer's later style is less fluid and graceful than that in his early works. In 1865 he was offered the Presidency of the Royal Academy, but he turned it down because of his health. He became an increasingly heavy drinker and the quality of his work declined during the 1860s. Before his death on October 1, 1873, he exhibited one hundred and seventy-seven works at the Royal Academy. A retrospective exhibition of his work in the winter of 1874 was the first one-man exhibition ever held by the Academy.

Bibliography

C. S. Maun, *The Works of Edwin Landseer*, London, 1843.

Algernon Graves, *Catalogue of the Works of Sir Edwin Landseer, RA*, Royal Academy, London, Winter 1874 (exhibition catalogue).

Allan Cunningham, *Lives of the Most Eminent British Painters*, London, 1879-1880, Vol. III, pp. 377-390 (revised edition, annotated and continued to the present time by Mrs. Charles Heaton).

W. Cosmo Monkhouse, *The Works of Sir Edwin Landseer*, London, 1879-1880.

Frederick G. Stephens, *Sir Edwin Landseer*, London, 1880 (3rd and extended edition of *The Early Works of Sir Edwin Landseer*, London, 1869).

James A. Manson, *Sir Edwin Landseer, RA*, London, 1902.

L. Scott, *Sir Edwin Landseer*, London, 1904.

Austin Chester, *The Art of Edwin Landseer*, London, 1920.

Charles Wheeler, John Woodward, Derek Hill, and Humphrey Brooke, *Sir Edwin Landseer, RA*, Royal Academy, London, 1961 (exhibition catalogue).

33. * QUEEN VICTORIA'S FAVORITE DOGS AND PARROT

Oil on canvas: 25 x 30 inches

Queen Victoria's Favorite Dogs and Parrot or *The Royal Pets*, as it is sometimes known, is a reduced replica of the picture of the same title exhibited at the Royal Academy in 1838 (Royal Collection). This was the first Academy exhibition that Victoria viewed as Queen, her uncle, William IV, having died shortly after the opening of the 1837 exhibition. The Queen was already familiar with Landseer's work. Her mother, the Duchess of Kent, had presented her with a portrait of her spaniel, "Dash," two years earlier. Landseer was to become a favorite, frequent guest, and occasional painting instructor to the Queen and the Prince Consort.

The composition of *Queen Victoria's Favorite Dogs and Parrot* is centered around the be-ribboned "Dash". Lying on a velvet covered footstool, he is surrounded by "Hester," "Nero," and "Lorey," the last named being the Duchess of Kent's parrot and the subject of an additional portrait presented by the Queen to her mother, also in 1838. While Landseer has not endowed these creatures with specifically human characteristics, as he was to do in many of his most famous pictures, such as *Dignity and Impudence* exhibited at the British Institution in 1831 (Tate Gallery), there is a suggestion of the animals'

mental activity which makes Landseer's painting quite different from, say, portraits of horses by George Stubbs (1724-1806). The dogs are not only beautiful, but also alert, sensitive, and intelligent; each is shown in a separate position and in an attitude that seems to reflect his individual state of mind. Following the lead of Sir Thomas Lawrence (1769-1830) and other Romantic portraitists, Landseer shows us not only what *his* sitters looked like, but by the tilt of a head or the glitter of an eye gives us a glimpse into their inner personalities.

William Makepeace Thackeray, in an article which first appeared in *Fraser's Magazine* in the form of a letter from M. A. Titmarsh, Esq. to Monsieur Anatole Victor Isidor Hyacinthe Achille Hercule de Bricabrac, expressed the opinion that *Queen Victoria's Favorite Dogs and Parrot* was Landseer's best picture in the Academy exhibition of 1838. He added, however, "I do not think he understands how to paint the great beast, man, quite so well . . . They [Landseer's paintings] are, if you like, the most dexterous pictures that ever were painted, but not great pictures" (reprinted in *The Paris Sketchbook and Art Criticisms*, The Oxford Thackeray, Vol. II, p. 383).

The image of "Dash," regally perched on his stool, became a popular needlework subject throughout the balance of Queen Victoria's reign.

After E. Landseer, *Dash*
needlework fire screen
(Collection Mrs. Christopher Forbes)

33. E. Landseer, *Queen Victoria's Favorite Dogs and Parrot.* (*see color Plate XI, p. 169*)

Provenance

Muriel, Lady Forteviot (Sale: Sotheby's Belgravia, London, November 28, 1972, Lot 153, reproduced)
Fine Art Society, London (Agents)

Exhibitions

The Art and Mind of Victorian England: Paintings from the Forbes Magazine Collection, University Gallery, University of Minnesota, Minneapolis, 1974, No. 27 (reproduced in color in catalogue).

References

Melvin Waldfogel, "Introduction," *The Art and Mind of Victorian England: Paintings from the Forbes Magazine Collection*, University Gallery, University of Minneapolis, Minneapolis, 1974, p. 20 (exhibition catalogue).

34. AZIM, A GREY ARAB MARE

Oil on board: 9 x 13-1/4 inches
Inscribed, lower left: *EL (monogram) 1861*

Although signed and dated, this small picture is really nothing more than a sketch. It did not appear in an annual Summer Exhibition of the Royal Academy, but was in the retrospective exhibition of Landseer's work there in the year following his death. The rendering of the horse's hide and the free treatment of the straw demonstrate the artist's powers, which were often at their most brilliant in his slighter works.

This is a portrait of a particular horse. It belongs to a tradition of English horse portraiture, of which the most distinguished practitioners were George Stubbs in the eighteenth century and James Ward in the first half of the nineteenth. Although heir to this tradition, Landseer was never primarily a painter of horses; he was much more at home with dogs. However, in the Victorian period there still was a market for portraits of horses which was catered to by several artists. The most successful was probably John Frederick Herring (1795-1865), whose many pictures of horses in their stalls seem to have provided the model followed by Landseer on this occasion.

Provenance

Sir Robert Peel, Bart.
Anon. Sale: Sotheby's, London, June 23, 1971, Lot 128.

Exhibitions

The Works of the Late Sir Edwin Landseer, RA, Winter Exhibition, Royal Academy, 1874, No. 361.

J. F. Herring, *A Grey in a Stable with Ducks*
(Photograph: Christie's)

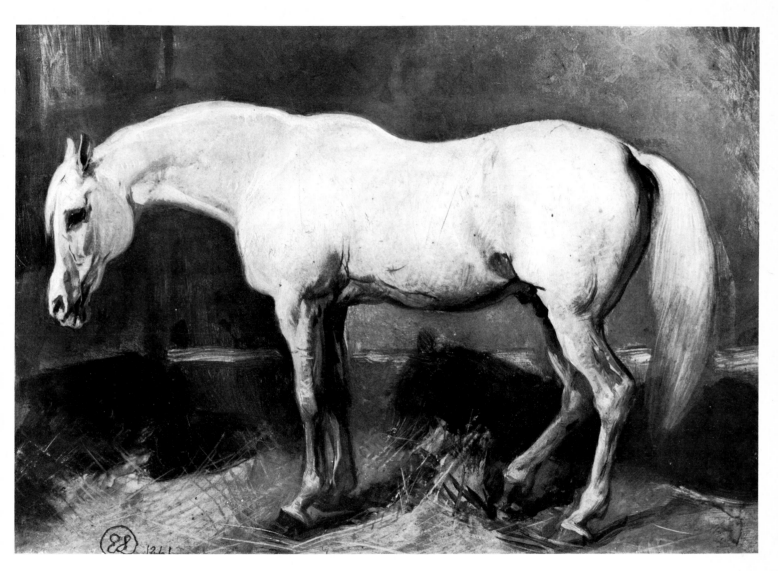

34. E. Landseer, *Azim, a Grey Arab Mare.*

BENJAMIN WILLIAMS LEADER, RA

(1831-1923)

was born in Reading on March 12, 1831. His real name was Benjamin Williams, but he added the surname "Leader" to it so as to distinguish himself from the family of the landscape painter Edward Williams (1782-1855), to whom he was not related. Five of Williams's sons became landscape painters and Leader did not wish to be confused with them. He began his studies with his father in Reading and entered the Royal Academy Schools in 1853. Although his father had known John Constable (1776-1837) and even copied some of his paintings, Leader's own landscapes bear little resemblance to those of the earlier master. The Pre-Raphaelites' precise, brilliant style attracted Leader for a while, but eventually he developed a looser, although still very detailed, style. His *February Fill-Dyke* of 1881, now in Birmingham, was the most popular landscape of the late Victorian period. Between 1854 and 1922 Leader exhibited two hundred and sixteen works at the Academy, all of them landscapes, except for a few early genre subjects.

He was elected an Associate of the Royal Academy in 1882 and a full Academician in 1897. Among the other honors awarded him during his long career (he did not die until March 22, 1923) were a Gold Medal at the *Exposition Universelle* of 1889 and the Cross of the Legion of Honor.

Bibliography

Lewis Lusk, "The Life and Work of Benjamin Williams Leader," *Art Annual: Supplement to the Art Journal,* 1901.

Frank Lewis, *Benjamin Williams Leader,* Leigh-on-Sea, 1971.

35. * THE SANDY MARGIN OF THE SEA

Oil on canvas: 48 x 71-3/4 inches
Inscribed, lower left: *B. W. LEADER, 1890*
Original frame

The Sandy Margin of the Sea was one of the three works shown by Leader at the Royal Academy Exhibition of 1890. It was not specifically commented on in any of the major Academy reviews. Two years earlier, Leader had shown a small picture (16 x 23 inches) entitled *The Sands of Aberdovey* at the Academy, and in 1921 he returned there with *The Bay of Aberdovey*. Although not listed as such in the Royal Academy catalogue, *The Sandy Margin of the*

Sea is also a view at Aberdovey on the West Coast of Wales. Leader painted Welsh subjects all his life, but the picture exhibited in 1888 was the first work he sent to the Academy with a title which identified it as a coastal scene. In 1889 he exhibited *Cambria's Coast,* and in 1890 one of his other exhibited pictures was entitled *When Sea and River Meet.* After 1900 Leader painted many landscapes on the South Coast of England. His *A Sandy Shore on the South Coast* of 1904 (Lewis, Pl. 84) and *Low Tide on the South Coast* of 1911 (Lewis, Pl. 91) are both similar to *The Sandy Margin of the Sea,* but sunnier and less dramatic in effect.

The subject of *The Sandy Margin of the Sea* makes it comparable to many works by John Brett (q.v.) and Henry Moore (q.v.), but it is more conventionally composed than the works of these two artists and lacks their quasi-scientific study of natural effects. Like most of Leader's mature landscapes it is a picture of mood. The empty foreground, deep space, cloudy sky, and threatening weather are characteristic not only of Leader's works but of many other later Victorian landscapes, whose bleak and dreary vistas evoked a poignant response in the hearts of prosperous and comfortable Victorians.

Provenance

Sir Godfrey Llewellyn, Bart. (Sale: Christie's, London, July 10, 1970, Lot 96).

Exhibitions

Royal Academy, 1890, No. 131.

References

Royal Academy Pictures: Supplement to the Magazine of Art, 1890, reproduced p. 50.

The Illustrated London News, May 10, 1890, p. 594.

Lewis Lusk, "The Life and Work of Benjamin Williams Leader," *Art Annual: Supplement to the Art Journal,* 1901, p. 32.

Frank Lewis, *Benjamin Williams Leader,* Leigh-on-Sea, 1971, pp. 29, 42, No. 292; p. 43, No. 300; pp. 61, 64. (Lewis apparently lists the picture twice: as *The Sandy Margin of the Sea,* No. 300 and *The Sandy Margin of the Sea — Aberdovey,* No. 292.)

35. B. W. Leader, *The Sandy Margin of the Sea.*

FREDERICK RICHARD LEE, RA
(1798-1879)

was born in Barnstaple, Devon, and he spent much of his life there. He had a short career in the army before entering the Royal Academy Schools in 1818. Six years later he made his debut at the Academy's annual exhibition with *Cottage from Nature.* He became an Associate in 1834 and a full Academician in 1838. Most of his pictures are idealized landscape views of Devon and Scotland. In 1847 he invited the animal painter Thomas Sidney Cooper (q.v.) to visit him in Devon and the two decided to collaborate on pictures with Lee painting the landscape and Cooper adding cattle and sheep. Their first joint works appeared at the Academy in the following year. Lee let Cooper handle all their business transactions and according to the latter: "Lee was fond of his profession to a certain extent, but more as a pastime than as a business . . . [he] gave the impression of considering the profession beneath him." In fact, Lee retired from the Royal Academy in 1872. With the small fortune he had accumulated during his successful career, he purchased a large yacht upon which he made extensive cruises. He died while on one of those at Capetown on June 4, 1879. During his lifetime he exhibited one hundred and seventy-one works at the Royal Academy, including fifteen in collaboration with Cooper.

Bibliography

Art Journal, 1879, p. 184, (obituary).
Thomas S. Cooper, *My Life,* 2 Vols., London, 1890, pp. 325-330.

36. *THE CHEQUERED SHADE

Oil on canvas: 78 x 66 inches
Inscribed, lower left: *F R. Lee RA 1854.*

The Chequered Shade was one of the fifteen works which Lee and Thomas Sidney Cooper (q.v.) showed jointly at the Royal Academy. The critic for the *Art Journal* praised it as "an incident described with an imitative truth, perfectly illusive." He also commented upon Lee's succesful rendering of the avenue of trees. The light filtering through the majestic old trees establishes the "chequered shade" of the picture's title. Cooper's contribution, the herd of sheep enjoying the shade, has little effect on the impact of Lee's landscape.

Views down avenue of trees are numerous in the history of art. A famous example which Lee was likely to have seen, as it had been exhibited at the British Institution in 1835, is *The Avenue at Middleharnis* by Meindert Hobbema, now in the National Gallery in London. There are also similar eighteenth-century pictures, for example *A Shady Avenue* by Fragonard in the Metropolitan Museum, which Lee could have known from the engraving by Greux. Two years before *The Chequered Shade* was shown at the Royal Academy, Holman Hunt had exhibited *The Hireling Shepherd* (City Art Gallery, Manchester), which has sheep and a perspective view between a row of trees in its background, though on a much smaller scale. Lee and Cooper belonged to a conservative faction of the Academy which was generally unsympathetic to the Pre-Raphaelites, but it is possible that Hunt's work provoked them to undertake this picture to demonstrate how such a motif should be treated.

Provenance

Arthur C. Burnand (Sale: Christie's, London, March 26, 1892, Lot 55, 250 gns.).
Thomas Clarke, Allerton Hall, Wollton, Liverpool (Sale: Christie's, London, January 29, 1926, Lot 46, £147).
Mrs. A. M. Matthews, granddaughter of Mr. Clarke (Sale: Christie's, London, November 20, 1970, Lot 278).

Exhibitions

Royal Academy, 1854, No. 362.
International Exhibition, London, 1862, No. 203.

References

Art Journal, 1854, p. 165.
The Illustrated London News Supplement, May 6, 1854, pp. 421, 424.
Athenaeum, May 13, 1854, p. 595.
Thomas Sidney Cooper, *My Life,* London, 1890, Vol. II, pp. ix, 315.

Forthcoming References

David Robertson, *Sir Charles Eastlake and the Victorian Art World,* Princeton University Press, 1975 (?) Fig. 178, Appendix E.3.

36. F. R. Lee and T. S. Cooper, *The Chequered Shade*.

FREDERIC, BARON LEIGHTON OF STRETTON, PRA

(1830-1896)

was the only British artist ever to be elevated to the peerage. This honor was conferred upon him just prior to his death in London on January 25, 1896.

He was born in Scarborough, Yorkshire, the son of a wealthy doctor and he was encouraged in his desire to become an artist. He studied abroad; first in Rome with Francesco Meli, then in Florence with Giuseppe Zanetti, and finally in Frankfurt at the Staedel Institute with a disciple of the Nazarenes, Edward von Steinle (1810-1886).

In 1855 he made his inaugural appearance at the Royal Academy exhibition with *Cimabue's Celebrated Madonna Carried in Procession through the Streets of Florence*. Queen Victoria purchased the picture for £600 and Leighton was launched on one of the most successful careers in British art history although he continued to live abroad, mainly in Paris and Italy, before settling permanently in London around 1860. During his years on the Continent, Leighton came into contact with many leading European artists, including Ary Scheffer (1795-1858), Peter Cornelius (1783-1867), William-Adolphe Bouguereau (1825-1905), and Jean-Léon Gérôme (1824-1904), and in England he was to exert a strong influence towards a cosmopolitan academicism. In the 1860s he moved away from medieval and biblical subjects in favor of classical ones. His works are often reminiscent of those of Bouguereau but his treatment of mythological subjects is less erotic than that of his French counterpart.

Leighton was elected an Associate of the Royal Academy in 1864 and an Academician in 1866. In 1878 he fulfilled a prediction made by the American sculptor, Hiram Powers (1805-1873), while Leighton was still a student in Florence, that he would be as famous an artist as he wished, when he succeeded Sir Francis Grant (1803-1878) as President of the Royal Academy. He was made an honorary member of almost every Academy in Europe, knighted in 1878, made a baronet in 1886, and, as noted, elevated to the peerage in 1896. A retrospective exhibition of his work was held at the Royal Academy in 1897. During his lifetime, he exhibited one hundred and sixty-four works there.

Bibliography

Mrs. A. Lang, "Sir Frederic Leighton: His Life and Works," *Art Annual: Supplement to the Art Journal*, 1884.
Ernest Rhys, *Sir Frederic Leighton, Bart., PRA*, London, 1895 (revised editions, 1900 and 1902).
George C. Williamson, *Frederic, Lord Leighton*, London, 1902.
Mrs. Russell Barrington, *The Life, Letters, and Works of Frederic Leighton*, 2 Vols., New York, 1906.
John Edgcombe Staley, *Lord Leighton of Stretton, PRA*, London, 1906.
Alfred L. Baldry, *Leighton*, London, 1908.

37. * BACCHANTE

Oil on canvas: 49-3/4 x 38 inches
Original frame

Bacchante was painted four years prior to Leighton's death. It displays the elaborately worked folds and rich, glazed colors which are the hallmarks of his mature work. The composition bears a strong resemblance to a *Diana* by Antonio Bellucci (1654-1726; Thomas Agnew & Sons, London) of approximately two centuries earlier, Leighton, however, has reversed the composition and more effectively related woman and animal.

Bacchante received little critical notice when it appeared at the Royal Academy in 1892, and what it did receive was mixed. *The Illustrated London News* ignored it and Blackburn, while describing it briefly, did not illustrate it in his *Academy Notes*. In the *Art Journal* Claude Phillips scathingly remarked, "A much lower level of achievement is apparent . . . in the *Bacchante,* which . . . completely lacks the rhythmic energy required to give adequate expression to the subject." The *Magazine of Art's* reviewer more generously decided "The single-figure pictures, *At the Fountain* and *The*

A. Bellucci, *Diana*
(Thos. Agnew & Sons, London)

Bacchante, are both distinguished by grace and refinement; the former tender, and the latter more robust in conception of color treatment."

As was the case with Leighton's major pictures, *Bacchante* was the product of numerous pencil, chalk and oil studies. (Leighton House, London: *Forbes* Magazine Collection, New York; etc.). A related drawing of a *Bacchante* is in the Collection of Allen Staley, and the most finished oil sketch, formerly in the Collection of J. Steward Hodgson, is reproduced in color in Mrs. Russell Barrington's biography of Leighton (Vol. II, opposite p. 287).

F. Leighton, *Bacchante* — drawing
(Collection Allen Staley)

F. Leighton, *Bacchante* — studies
(*Forbes* Magazine Collection, New York)

37. F. Leighton, *Bacchante*.
(*see color Plate XII, p. 170*)

Provenance

Arthur Manners

Anon. Sale: Christie's, London, October 11, 1968, Lot 106.

Old Hall Gallery, Ltd., Iden, Rye, Sussex (Oil Paintings List 699, No. 75K, reproduced).

Stanley G. Harris. Portland, Oregon.

Anon. Sale: Sotheby's Belgravia, London, July 9, 1974, Lot 48, reproduced.

Exhibitions

Royal Academy, 1892, No. 257.

References

Art Journal, 1892, pp. 188-190.

Henry Blackburn, *Academy Notes,* London, 1892, p. 12.

Magazine of Art, Vol. XV, 1892, p. 221.

Ernest Rhys, *Sir Frederic Leighton, Bart., PRA,* London, 1895, p. 72, reproduced opposite p. 60 (revised editions, 1900 and 1902).

Alice Corkran, *Frederic Leighton,* London, 1904, p. 197.

Mrs. Russell Barrington, *The Life, Letters, and Works of Frederic Leighton,* London, 1906, Vol. II, pp. 260, 391, reproduced following p. 286.

Forthcoming References

Richard Ormond, *Lord Leighton,* Yale University Press, 1975 (?).

38. TRAGIC POETESS

Oil on canvas: 8-7/8 x 5 inches

This painting is the oil sketch for *Tragic Poetess* or *Tragic Muse* as it is sometimes called, which was first exhibited at the Royal Academy in 1890. The finished work was sold at Sotheby's, London, on June 17, 1970, and is now in a private collection in Japan. The critic for the *Art Journal* felt that "it altogether fails to attain the solemnity of such a subject, when attempted from the higher point of view" (1890, p. 162). What this "higher point of view" is the writer did not say. In marked contrast to this review was that of the critic for the *Magazine of Art,* who declared, "the angry sea, the lurid sky flecked with blood, the lowering brow and brooding eyes, as the woman guards the ominous record-scrolls, are all ingenious in their imagery" (1890, Vol. XIII, p. 219).

The oil sketch evokes all these "ingenious" qualities and in many ways, especially in its freer handling, it is a more evocative picture than the more highly finished work that evolved from it. A drawing for the composition is reproduced in Rhys (1895, p. xxvi, d), and other related drawings are in Leighton House, London. The concept of the enthroned figure stems from the famous painting of *Sarah Siddons as the Tragic Muse* (Huntington Library and Art Gallery, San Marino, California) by one of Leighton's predecessors as President of the Royal Academy, Sir Joshua Reynolds (1729-1792), who, in turn, was inspired by the Prophets and Sibyls by Michelangelo on the ceiling of the Sistine Chapel. Many of Leighton's later pictures are of single female figures in classical guise, most of whom look more like great *tragédiennes* of the stage than actual historical figures.

Provenance

J. Stewart Hodgson

Durlacher Bros., New York

Robert Isaacson, New York

Anthony D'Offay, London

Mrs. Robert Frank, London

Forbes Magazine Collection, New York

Anon. Sale: Sotheby's Belgravia, London, July 9, 1974, Lot 49, reproduced.

Exhibitions

Works by the Late Lord Leighton of Stretton, Winter Exhibition, Royal Academy, 1897, No. 92.

Painters of the Beautiful, Durlacher Bros., New York, 1964, No. 4.

The Art and Mind of Victorian England: Paintings from the Forbes Magazine Collection, University Gallery, University of Minnesota, Minneapolis, 1974, No. 29 (reproduced in catalogue).

References

Mrs. Russell Barrington, *The Life, Letters and Works of Frederic Leighton,* London, 1906, Vol. II, reproduced in color opposite p. 259.

Forthcoming References

Richard Ormond, *Lord Leighton,* Yale University Press, 1975 (?).

F. Leighton, *Tragic Poetess* (Private Collection, Japan)

38. F. Leighton, *Tragic Poetess*.

CHARLES ROBERT LESLIE, RA
(1794-1859)

was born in London in 1794 of American parents. He grew up in Philadelphia where he had his first lessons in painting from Thomas Sully (1783-1872). In 1811 a group of Philadelphia merchants took up a subscription to send the young artist to London to study for the next two years. However, once in England, Leslie remained for the rest of his life, returning to America for five months in 1833-34, when he had a brief appointment as drawing master at West Point. Leslie's first associates in London were the expatriate American artists Benjamin West (1738-1820) and Washington Allston (1779-1843), to whom he took letters of introduction from Sully. He was also a friend of Washington Irving, and contemporaries considered their styles and outlooks analogous.

Throughout his career Leslie specialized in painting scenes drawn from literary sources. His most popular works were illustrations of *Don Quixote,* but his sources of subjects also included Shakespeare, Molière, and Goldsmith. Unlike earlier illustrations of literature such as those by Henry Fuseli (1741-1825), who projected into his subjects a highly personal vision, Leslie's pictures are straightforward depictions whose success depended on the viewers' recognizing a favorite passage or scene from a work with which he was already well acquainted, either from reading or seeing it performed on the stage. Leslie's art represents perfectly the toning down of romantic emotion into Victorian domestic sentimentality, and it was immensely popular. He made his debut at the Royal Academy in 1813 with *Murder,* a scene drawn from *Macbeth* and seven years later, he was elected an Associate Academician. He became a full Academician in 1826. From 1833 to 1847 he served as Professor of Painting of that institution. Leslie was the father of George Dunlop Leslie (1835-1921) and a close friend of John Constable (1776-1837). His life of the landscape painter, published in 1845, is a classic artistic biography which remains the prime source for the artist's life. Although Leslie was a conservative and essentially timid artist in comparison to Constable, the latter's influence did lead to a discernible new breadth and luminosity in Leslie's mature works. His lectures to the Royal Academy students, published in 1855 as *A Handbook for Young Painters*, expressed a by then conservative point of view which drew a scornful attack from Ruskin, at the time in full fig as defender of the Pre-Raphaelites. Leslie died in London four years later having exhibited seventy-six works at the Royal Academy.

Bibliography

Art Journal, 1859, p. 187 (obituary)
Tom Taylor, ed. *Autobiographical Recollections by the late Charles Robert Leslie, RA, with a Prefatory Essay on Leslie as an Artist,* and *Selections from his Correspondence,* 2 Vols., London, 1860.
Allan Cunningham, *Lives of the Most Eminent British Painters,* 1879-1880, Vol. III, pp. 338-362 (revised edition, annotated and continued to the present time by Mrs. Charles Heaton).
Richard Redgrave and Samuel Redgrave, *A Century of Painters of the English School,* 1883, pp. 333-340 (2nd edition).

39. * SANCHO PANZA IN THE APARTMENT OF THE DUCHESS

Oil on canvas stretched on panel: 24-1/4 x 30 inches
Inscribed on verso, lower left: *Painted by C. R. Leslie, November 1857*

Cervantes was a source of continual inspiration to Leslie. At the Royal Academy alone, he exhibited eight pictures based on *Don Quixote. Sancho Panza in the Apartment of the Duchess* was one of Leslie's favorite incidents, and one he painted no less than four times. This version is the last recorded one and was painted for his sister in 1857 two years before his death. The first (Petworth Collection) was painted for Lord Egremont, the great patron of Joseph Mallord Turner, and was exhibited at the Royal Academy in 1824 accompanied by the following quotation from Part II, Chapter 33 of *Don Quixote:*

> First and foremost, I must tell you I look upon my master, Don Quixote, to be no better than a downright madman, though sometimes he will stumble on a parcel of sayings so quaint and so tightly put together, that the devil himself could not mend them; but in the man, I cannot beat it out of my noodle, but that he is as mad as a March hare.

(continued on page 149)

C. R. Leslie, *Sancho Panza in the Apartment of the Duchess* — 1824 (From the Petworth Collection)

C. R. Leslie, *Sancho Panza in the Apartment of the Duchess* — 1844 (The Tate Gallery, London)

C. R. Leslie, *Sancho Panza in the Apartment of the Duchess* — before 1856 (Photograph: Sotheby's Belgravia)

C. R. Leslie, *Sancho Panza in the Apartment of the Duchess* — sketch (The Tate Gallery, London)

39. C. R. Leslie, *Sancho Panza in the Apartment of the Duchess*.

JOHN FREDERICK LEWIS, RA
(1805-1876)

was born on July 14, 1805 in the same house where Edwin Landseer (q.v.) had been born three years earlier. His father, Frederick Christian Lewis, like Landseer's was a prominent engraver and also his son's first instructor. Unlike Landseer, however, Lewis was expected to follow his father's lead and become an engraver, and it was not until he succeeded (before he was fifteen years old) in having a small work, entitled *A Donkey's Head,* exhibited and sold at the British Institution that he was allowed to pursue a career as a painter.

Lewis and Landseer were friends as boys and together spent hours drawing exotic beasts in the menagerie at Exeter 'Change in the Strand. The Redgraves record in *A Century of Painters* that when one of the lions died: "He and Landseer bought it and preserved it so long for purposes of drawing and dissection that at last their neighbors, whose artistic sense was less developed perhaps than their olfactory one, were forced to complain" (second edition, 1890, p. 377).

Most of Lewis's early works were of animals. In 1821 he exhibited *Puppies, A Study from Nature* at the Royal Academy. It was the first of some eighty-two works that he eventually was to show there. Six years later the artist took his first trip abroad, a tour of the Rhineland, the Tyrol and Lombardy, which carried him as far as Venice. About this time he began to turn increasingly to watercolor, and he was elected an Associate of the Old Watercolour Society in 1827.

From 1832 to 1834 Lewis was in Spain. In 1837 he left England again and did not return for almost a decade and a half. He spent the first three years on the Continent mostly in Paris and Rome; then, after two years in Rome, he sailed for Constantinople in 1840. After touring Asia Minor in the summer of 1841, he moved to Cairo, where he remained until returning to London in 1851. Just prior to his departure from Cairo, Lewis sent a large work entitled *The Hhareem* to the exhibition of the Old Watercolour Society in 1850. It caused a sensation, being both the first work exhibited in London by Lewis since 1841, and, more importantly, the first to demonstrate the brilliant technique which the artist developed in the East. The picture was eventually sold for £1,000, a staggering sum for a watercolor. All Lewis's subsequent works were of Eastern subjects. After his return to London, he exhibited only watercolors at first. He was elected President of the Old Watercolour Society in 1855, but in the same year, he began exhibiting oils at the Royal Academy (after not showing there at all since 1834), and in 1858 he resigned as both President and Member of the Old Water-colour Society, so that he could devote his time to the more lucrative field of oil painting. He was elected as an Associate of the Royal Academy in 1859 and a full Academician in 1865. In the spring of 1876, he had himself placed on the list of retired members because of his declining health. He died at Walton-on-Thames on August 15, 1876. Ruskin paid Lewis perhaps the ultimate tribute when he declared: "I believe John Lewis to have done more entire justice to his powers (and they are magnificent ones) than any other man amongst us" (*Works,* Vol. XII, p. 363).

Bibliography

W. M. Thackeray, *Notes of a Journey from Cornhill to Grand Cairo,* London, 1846.
"British Artists: Their Style and Character; No. XXXII — John Frederick Lewis," *Art Journal,* 1858, pp. 41-43.
Art Journal, 1876, p. 329 (obituary).
Randall Davies, "John Frederick Lewis, R.A. Some Contemporary Notices with Comments by the Editor," *The Old Water Colour Society's Club,* Vol. III, 1926, pp. 31-50.
Hugh Stokes, "John Frederick Lewis, R.A." *Walker's Quarterly,* No. 28, 1929.
Brinsley Ford, "J. F. Lewis and Richard Ford in Seville, 1832-33," *Burlington Magazine,* February 1942, pp. 124-129.
Richard Green, *John Frederick Lewis, RA,* Laing Art Gallery, Newcastle-upon-Tyne, 1971 (exhibition catalogue).

40. * THE STREET AND THE MOSQUE OF THE GHOREEYAH, CAIRO

Watercolor and oil on paper laid on panel:
29-3/4 x 40-1/2

The Street and the Mosque of the Ghoreeyah, Cairo is apparently an earlier version of an unfinished picture of the same title which was exhibited posthumously at the Royal Academy in the summer of 1877, the year after Lewis's death (Private Collection, USA). The *Art Journal* described the latter as "showing all that exquisite detail, brilliant colouring and deft play of light for which his pictures were always so conspicuous" (1877, p. 269).

The Academy picture is a vertical rather than a horizontal composition; more of the street as well as more people are depicted in it. A watercolor of the *Street and Mosque of the Ghoreeyah, Cairo* (Courtauld Institute of Art, Witt Collection) probably was painted by Lewis while he was living in Cairo (1841-1851) and used by him as a study for both pictures.

Provenance

Anon. Sale: Sotheby's, London, June 23, 1971, Lot 76, reproduced.
Fine Art Society, London (Agents).

Exhibitions

The Art and Mind of Victorian England: Paintings from the Forbes Magazine Collection, University Gallery, University of Minnesota, Minneapolis, 1974, No. 31 (reproduced in catalogue).

References

Richard Green, *John Frederick Lewis, RA, 1805-1876,* Laing Art Gallery, Newcastle-upon-Tyne, 1971, p. 25 (exhibition catalogue).

J. F. Lewis, *The Street and the Mosque of the Ghoreeyah, Cairo* — watercolor (Witt Collection, Courtauld Institute of Art)

J. F. Lewis, *The Street and the Mosque of the Ghoreeyah, Cairo* (Private Collection, USA, Photograph: Fine Art Society)

40. J. F. Lewis, *The Street and Mosque of
the Ghoreeyah, Cairo.*
(*see color Plate XIII, p. 171*)

JAMES THOMAS LINNELL
(after 1826-1905)

was the son of the landscape painter, John Linnell (q.v.). He was born in Hampstead and moved with his father to Redhill, Surrey, in the 1850s. His brothers, John, Jr. and William Linnell (1826-1910) also became painters. All studied under their father, and worked in similar landscape styles although that of James is said to have been more brightly colored and boldly painted, probably reflecting Pre-Raphaelite influence. During the 1850s he painted some religious scenes but then devoted himself to landscapes. He first exhibited at the Royal Academy in 1850. He stopped suddenly thirty-eight years later, having shown exactly thirty-eight works there.

Bibliography

James Dafforne, "British Artists: Their Styles and Character; No. CVII—James Thomas Linnell," *Art Journal*, 1872, p. 250-251.
Alfred T. Story, *The Life of John Linnell*, 2 Vols., London, 1892.

41. THE RAINBOW

Oil on canvas: 44 x 63-1/2 inches
Inscribed, lower right: *James Linnell 1863*
Original frame

The Rainbow was exhibited at the Royal Academy in 1863 with the following biblical quotation:

> And it shall come to pass, when I bring a cloud over the earth, that the bow shall be seen in the cloud — (Genesis, ix, 14)

Critical response to the picture was hostile. *The Reader* declared.

> The Linnells are more striking and less agreeable than usual. Evanescene is the characteristic of such effects as *The Rainbow* (22) by Mr. J. T. Linnell. Turner [1775-1851] and Cox [David Cox Sr., 1783-1859] succeeded in suggesting to us passing showers or approaching storms. In the picture before us, we are conscious of an exaggeration and weight which destroy all the tenderness of nature; and we are left with an impression of what the painter wished, but has failed to express.

The Illustrated London News was no less uncomplimentary.

> The Messrs. Linnell have assimilated their style more than ever, and continue to confine themselves to a uniform set of effects, which, though rendered with great technical skill, are open to the charge of exaggeration. The contribution by this family, most daring and violent in its oppositions of hot and bright, heavy and cold colour, is No. 22, by Mr. J. T. Linnell, an artist who (apparently through

imitation of his father) has quite lost the delicate truth to nature of his early works, and together with it much of his individuality. This picture represents sheep and cattle gathered together under the shelter of a rugged slope, gnarled with tree roots, on which and on the retiring bank of slaty thundercloud the sun has burst, lighting up a brilliant rainbow.

In an essay in the forthcoming book, *Nature and the Victorian Imagination,* Professor George Landow cites Rubens's *Landscape with a Rainbow* (Wallace Collection, London) as an "obvious influence" and goes on to question how essential are the title and the text from *Gensis* to the picture itself. As the reviews indicate, this picture is also very similar to many works by James Linnell's father.

Provenance

Charles Collard, (Sale: Christie's, London, February 13, 1892, Lot 164).
Thomas Clarke, Allerton Hall, Woolton, Liverpool, (Sale: Christie's, London, January 29, 1926, Lot 48, £189).
Mrs. A. M. Mathews, granddaughter of Mr. Clarke, (Sale: Christie's, London, November 20, 1970, Lot 280).
Anon. Sale: Christie's, London, July 23, 1971, Lot 350.
Fine Art Society, London (Agents)

Exhibitions

Royal Academy, 1863, No. 22.
National Exhibition of Works of Art, Leeds, 1868, No. 1412.

References

The Illustrated London News, May 23, 1863, p. 574.
The Reader, June 13, 1863, p. 581.
James Dafforne, "British Artists: Their Style and Character, No. CVII—James Thomas Linnell," *Art Journal,* 1872, p. 251.

Forthcoming References

George Landow and others, *Nature and the Victorian Imagination,* University of California Press, 1976.

41. J. T. Linnell, *The Rainbow*.

JOHN LINNELL
(1792-1882)

was born in Bloomsbury in 1792. His father was a frame-maker, gilder, and vendor of prints and pictures. Before John was twelve, Linnell, Sr. had him copying the works of British eighteenth-century genre painters. In 1805 he was apprenticed to Blake's friend, the watercolor painter John Varley (1778-1842). William Henry (Bird's nest) Hunt (1790-1864) and William Mulready (1786-1863) were also students of Varley, and the work of the latter had as great an influence on Linnell as that of their master. He entered the Royal Academy Schools in 1805 where he was encouraged by Benjamin West (1738-1820). He made his debut at the Academy two years later with *A Study from Nature*. He also exhibited at the British Institution and the Old Watercolour Society, and was a member of the latter body from 1813 to 1820 during a period when the Society admitted oil paintings. According to Story, it was principally as a portrait painter, however, that Linnell supported himself until 1847. Only then did he feel established enough to pursue landscape almost exclusively.

Shortly after this, he moved with his family to Redhill in Surrey where he lorded over them for two generations in despotic and miserly fashion until his death in 1882. He was a patron of his master Varley's friend, William Blake, and is frequently said to have subverted and destroyed the genius of his son-in-law, Samuel Palmer (1805-1881).

From 1821 to 1841 he allowed his name to be proposed, unsuccessfully, as a candidate for Associate in the Royal Academy. Twenty years later, when he was more established, the Academy solicited Linnell's membership but he was too old and embittered to accept. He attributed his failure to gain recognition earlier to the hatred of John Constable (1776-1837). Unlike the latter, he had little interest in specific places, but rather concentrated on "aspects of nature." During his career he exhibited one hundred and seventy-seven works at the Royal Academy and a retrospective exhibition of his paintings was held there in the winter of 1883 together with the works of another non-member, Dante Gabriel Rossetti (1828-1882).

Bibliography

"British Artists: Their Style and Character; No. XLIV — John Linnell," *Art Journal*, 1859, pp. 105-107.
Frederick G. Stephens, "John Linnell," *Portfolio*, 1872, pp. 45-48.
Frederick G. Stephens, "John Linnell, Painter and Engraver," *Art Journal*, 1882, pp. 261-264, 293-296.
Frederick G. Stephens, "The Aims, Studies, and Progress of John Linnell, Painter and Engraver," *Art Journal*, 1883, pp. 37-40.

Alfred T. Story, "John Linnell's Country," *Art Journal*, 1892, pp. 301-305.
Alfred T. Story, *The Life of John Linnell*, 2 Vols., London, 1892.
A Loan Exhibition of Drawings, Watercolors, and Paintings by John Linnell and His Circle, P. & D. Colnaghi, London, 1973 (exhibition catalogue).

42. * THE RETURN OF ULYSSES

Oil on canvas: 49 x 73 inches
Inscribed, lower right: *J. Linnell, 1848* and:

ΔΗ ΤΟΤΕ Σ ΑΤΡΕΜΑΣ ΕΥΔΕ
ΛΕΛΑΣΜΕΝΟΣ ΟΣΣ ΕΠΕΠΟΝΘΕΙ

[ΠΡΩΤΟΝ] ΟΔΥΣΣΗΑ ΣΛΑΦΥΡΗΣ
ΕΚ ΝΗΟΣ ΑΕΙΡΑΝ

[ΑΥΤΩ] ΣΥΝ ΤΕ ΛΙΝΩ ΚΑΙ ΡΗΣΕΙ
ΣΙΣΑΛΟΕΝΤΙ

[ΚΑΔ Δ ΑΡ ΕΠΙ] ΨΑΜΑΘΩ ΕΘΕΣΑΝ
ΔΕΔΜΗΜΕΝΟΝ ΥΠΝΩ

ΩΜΗΡΟΥ
ΟΔΥΣΣΕΙΑΣ

The Return of Uylsses is one of the few classical subjects undertaken by Linnell. It is a highly romanticized picture depicting the great warrior being put ashore at Ithaca. When it was shown at the Royal Academy in 1849 it was accompanied in the catalogue with the following quotation from Homer's *Odyssey:*

> And first brought forth Uylsses: bed, and all
> That richly furnish't it; he still in thrall
> Of all-subduing sleepe. Upon the sand
> They set him softly down; and then, the strand
> They strewed with all the goods he had, bestowed
> By the renowned Phoenicians.

Segments of these lines are inscribed in Greek on the tablets in the lower right-hand corner of the picture. The critic writing for the *Art Journal* did not feel that it was as "attractive as other productions of the artist" because it was "without immediate reference to nature." Both the story and the landscape are secondary to the dominant feature of the picture: the brilliant setting sun. Its forceful light overwhelms the rest of the composition and gives the picture a sense of spectacle and drama.

The classical subject and the balanced composition looking into the source of light recall the ideal landscape compositions of Claude Lorraine, such as *The Departure of the Queen of Sheba* which was one of the first pictures to enter the National Gallery in London. The influence of Claude was strong in the earlier nineteenth century and is evident, for example, in many pictures by Turner, but it waned rapidly in the Victorian period, in part because of Ruskin's violent attacks published in 1843 in the first volume of *Modern Painters*. In most of Linnell's works, neither Claudian nor Turnerian influence is particularly evident, but it should be remembered that this picture was painted only the year after he gave up portrait painting and before he established the repetitious pattern of his later landscapes.

Provenance

John Graham, Skelmorlie Castle, Scotland (Sale: Christie's, London, April 30, 1887, Lot 76, 1,400 gns.).
Thomas Agnew & Sons, London.
Sir John Barran, Bart. (Sale: Christie's, London, July 1, 1905, Lot 16, 250 gns.).
Anon. Sale: Christie's, London, May 30, 1924, Lot 168.
Bruce Graham-Hersey, Dublin.
Anon. Sale: Christie's, London, March 5, 1971, Lot 16.
Fine Art Society, London (Agents).

Exhibitions

Royal Academy, 1849, No. 443
Art Treasures, Manchester, 1857, No. 471
Fine Art Loan Exhibition in Aid of the Royal Infirmary, Glasgow, 1878.
Works by the late John Linnell, Winter Exhibition, Royal Academy, 1883, No. 64.

References

Art Journal, 1849, p. 174.
The Illustrated London News, May 26, 1849, p. 350.
Art Journal, 1883, p. 38.
The Daily Mirror, London, July 3, 1905, p. 3.
Evan R. Firestone, "John Linnell and the Picture Merchants," *Connoisseur*, February, 1973, p. 130.

42. J. Linnell, *The Return of Ulysses.*
(see color Plate XIV, p. 172)

DANIEL MACLISE, RA
(1806-1870)

was born in Ireland on February 2, 1806, the son of Alexander McClish, a shoemaker. He studied at the Cork School of Art which was established in 1822. Maclise then set up his own portrait studio. The artist came to London in 1827, and entered the Royal Academy Schools the following year. In 1829 he won the Silver Medal for drawing from the antique and made his debut at the Academy's annual exhibition with *Malvolio Affecting the Count.* Two years later he won the Schools' Gold Medal for history painting with the *Choice of Hercules.* In 1835 he began to spell his name Maclise instead of McClish. He exhibited a large number of successful history compositions at the Royal Academy, and his career flourished. In 1843 Queen Victoria purchased his *Scene from Undine* to present to Prince Albert on his birthday. The Prince in his turn commissioned Maclise to execute one of the frescoes in the Garden Pavilion at Buckingham Palace (see Appendix II). This was followed by commissions for two frescoes in the New Palace of Westminster: *The Spirit of Chivalry* completed in 1848 and *The Spirit of Justice* completed in 1849 (see Appendix II). In 1857 he agreed to paint two huge frescoes in the Royal Gallery in the new Parliament buildings, and in 1859 he began *The Meeting of Wellington and Blücher.* Work on this and its pendant, *The Death of Nelson,* was not completed until 1865 and the effort completely undermined his health.

In 1835 he was elected an Associate of the Royal Academy and in 1840, a full Member. In 1866, he declined to be put forward for its Presidency. During his career he exhibited eighty-four works there and in 1875, a group of fifteen of his paintings was shown at the Academy's Winter Exhibition.

Bibliography

"Portraits of British Artists; No. 3—Daniel Maclise," *Art Union,* 1847, p. 164.
W. Justin O'Driscoll, *A Memoir of Daniel Maclise, RA,* London, 1871.
Richard Ormond, "Daniel Maclise," *Burlington Magazine,* December, 1968, pp. 685-693.
Richard Ormond, "Daniel Maclise (1806-1870)—A Major Figurative Painter," *Connoisseur,* March, 1972, pp. 165-171.
Richard Ormond, *Daniel Maclise,* The Arts Council of Great Britain, London, 1972 (exhibition catalogue).
Richard Ormond and John Turpin, *Daniel Maclise,* The Arts Council of Great Britain, London, 1972 (exhibition catalogue).
John Turpin, "German Influence on Daniel Maclise," *Apollo,* February, 1973, pp. 169-175.

43. *THE PLAY SCENE IN HAMLET

Watercolor, body color and varnish on paper: 14-1/4 x 25-1/2 inches
Original frame

This watercolor is an exact replica of *The Play Scene in Hamlet* (Tate Gallery), which Maclise exhibited at the Royal Academy in 1842. The large picture (60 x 108 inches) and the equally large and melodramatic *Banquet Scene in Macbeth* (Guildhall Art Gallery, London), which had preceded it by two years, established Maclise's reputation as the foremost historical painter of the Victorian period. Throughout his career *The Play Scene* remained one of his most popular pictures. The critic for the *Art Union* categorized it as "in all respects, a chef-d'oeuvre of the British school" (1842, p. 120), while the critic for *The Times* was no less enthusiastic when he called it "the lion of the gallery" (May 3, 1842, p. 5). Charles Dickens, who was a close friend of the artist, raved: "A tremendous production. There are things in it, which in their powerful thought exceed anything I have ever beheld in painting" (*Letters,* Nonesuch edition, 1938, Vol. I, p. 469). William Makepeace Thackeray went so far as to call it "one of the most startling, wonderful pictures that the English schools has every produced" (reprinted in *The Paris Sketchbook and Art Criticisms,* The Oxford Thackeray, Vol. II, p. 576). On the other hand, Ruskin sounded a sour note when he described the figure of Hamlet as an "Irish ruffian" and dismissed the picture as a "grinning and glittering fantasy" (*Works,* Vol. III, p. 619n). Allan Cunningham was also harsh on the picture: "The action is too strained, the passion too apparent to be true to nature. It is, in fact, just an interpretation of Shakespeare as might be expected from a clever but not really great actor" (*Lives of the Most Eminent British Painters,* Mrs. Heaton, ed., 1879-80, Vol. III, p. 419).

The composition depends on the *Outlines to Shakespeare* by the German artist, Moritz Retzsch (1779-1857). It is also close to a plate in the album of lithographs by Eugene Deveria (1805-1865) and Louis Boulanger (1806-1867), based on performances of Charles Kemble's company in Paris in 1827. The tapestries to the left and right of the stage in the composition depict *The Temptation in the Garden of Eden, The Expulsion, The Sacrifice of Abel,* and, lastly, *Cain Murdering Abel.* In a niche above Ophelia, to the left of the stage, is a statue of Prayer; on the other side, above the tormented king, is a figure of Justice.

Provenance
James Gresham, C.E., J.P.
Fine Art Society, London

Exhibitions
International Fine Arts Exhibition, Rome, 1911, No. 54 (British Section).
Aspects of Victorian Art, Fine Art Society, London, 1971, No. 100.
Daniel Maclise, Arts Council of Great Britain, 1972, No. 77 (reproduced in catalogue).
Victorian Art, The Emily Lowe Gallery, Hofstra University, Hempstead, New York, 1972, No. 76.
The Art and Mind of Victorian England: Paintings from the Forbes Magazine Collection, University Gallery, University of Minnesota, Minneapolis, 1974, No. 32 (reproduced in catalogue).

References
Sir Isidore Spielmann, *International Fine Arts Exhibition, Rome: Souvenir of the British Section,* London, 1911, pp. 128, 136, reproduced p. 48 (gallery view, see lower right).
Richard Ormond and John Turpin, *Daniel Maclise,* The Arts Council of Great Britain, London, 1972, pp. 71-72 (exhibition catalogue).
Richard Ormond, "Daniel Maclise (1806-1870)—A Major Figurative Painter," *Connoisseur,* March, 1972, pp. 165-171, reproduced p. 166.
John Turpin, "German Influence on Daniel Maclise," *Apollo,* February, 1973, pp. 169, 170, reproduced p. 169.
Michael A. Findlay, "*Forbes Saves the Queen,*" Arts Magazine, February, 1973, pp. 26-30, reproduced p. 28.
Melvin Waldfogel, "Introduction," *The Art and Mind of Victorian England: Paintings from the Forbes Magazine Collection,* University of Minnesota, Minneapolis, 1974, p. 21 (exhibition catalogue).

D. Maclise, *The Play Scene in Hamlet* (The Tate Gallery, London)

43. D. Maclise, *The Play Scene in Hamlet.*
(*see color Plate XV, p. 173*)

JOHN MacWHIRTER, RA
(1839-1911)

was born on March 27, 1839 at Slatesford, near Edinburgh. His father, a paper manufacturer whose hobbies were drawing, botany and geology, died when MacWhirter was thirteen, and the boy had to leave his school at Peebles and go to work. He was apprenticed to a bookseller in Edinburgh for five years, but after six months he bolted, determined to become an artist. Barely fifteen, MacWhirter became one of the youngest persons to exhibit at the Royal Scottish Academy when his *Old Cottage at Braid* was shown there in 1854. He then was accepted at the Trustee's Academy in Edinburgh where he studied under Robert Scott Lauder (1803-1869). Among his classmates were William Quiller Orchardson (q.v.) and William MacTaggart (1835-1910). MacWhirter's taste for travel was unquenchable. In the late 1850s, while still in his teens, he began visiting the Continent annually. Eventually he even crossed the Atlantic and ended up sketching in the Yosemite Valley. In 1865 he made his debut at the Royal Academy with a small work entitled *Temple of Vesta, Rome.* Two years later he was elected an Associate Member of the Royal Scottish Academy. His large landscapes began to attract favorable attention in London and the artist moved there from Edinburgh in 1869. A decade later he was elected an Associate Member of the Royal Academy while in 1880 he was made an Honorary Member of the Royal Scottish Academy. It was not until 1897, however, that he was elected to the full Membership in the Royal Academy. In 1900 he wrote a manual for Messrs. Cassell entitled, *Landscape Painting in Watercolour.*

During his career, he exhibited one hundred and fifty-three pictures at the Royal Academy's annual exhibition, all of them landscapes. As Landseer had succeeded in endowing his animals with human qualities, so MacWhirter succeeded with his trees, including such examples as *The Three Witches* and the pair *The Lord of the Glen* and *The Lady of the Woods.* The popularity and saleability of works such as these, painted in a dark-hued loose manner reminiscent of Millais's late landscape style, enabled MacWhirter to build an enormous Italian Renaissance style mansion in St. John's Wood and to leave a substantial sum of money to his daughter after his death on January 28, 1911.

Bibliography

James Dafforne, "The Works of John MacWhirter, ARSA," *Art Journal*, 1879, pp. 9-11.
William MacDonald Sinclair, "John MacWhirter, RA," *Art Annual: Supplement to the Art Journal*, 1905.
S. Cursiter, *Scottish Art*, New York, 1949, pp. 125-127.

44. *THE TRACK OF A HURRICANE

Oil on canvas: 59-3/4 x 84 inches
Inscribed, lower left: *MacW*
Original slip frame

The bleak mood of *The Track of a Hurricane* is typical of much of MacWhirter's *oeuvre.* The uprooted tree which dominates the center foreground of the canvas reappeared a decade and a half later in *A Fallen Giant.*

The critic writing for the *Art Journal* when *The Track of a Hurricane* was hung at the Royal Academy in 1885 described MacWhirter as being "in far greater force than either of his colleagues." Whether this reference was directed to the number of works the artist had in the exhibition (five) or to the power of the painting itself is not clear. However, the reviewer went on to declare that the picture "marks out a fresh departure of his Art" and he concluded his comments with a dramatic description of the event depicted. The reviewer of *The Illustrated London News* more briefly and perhaps more sarcastically noted: "Mr. MacWhirter's *Track of the Hurricane* is the head of a rocky defile strewn with broken boughs and uprooted trees, once the scene of a giant strife, but now all peaceful and smiling."

The ravaged landscape depicted here is an extreme example of the later Victorian tendency to see nature as bleak and inhospitable, not inviting and pleasant as it had been painted by earlier Victorian artists such as Frederick Richard Lee (see No. 36). Charles Darwin's *On the Origin of Species,* published in 1859, and Herbert Spencer's philosophy of "survival of the fittest" gave a new concept of nature to a younger generation of landscape painters. In MacWhirter's picture the few trees that remain standing, like the tiny deer on the distant cliff, are not inhabitants of a universe running smoothly in accordance with divine plan, but survivors of nature's mindless destructive power. Although philosophically up-to-date, *The Track of a Hurricane* harks back thematically to eighteenth- and earlier nineteenth-century pictures of the destructive violence of nature such as Turner's *Fall of an Avalanche in the Grisons* of c. 1810 (Tate Gallery). Stylistically, the rocky cliffs and blasted trees recall the seventeenth-century landscapes of Salvator Rosa, which eighteenty-century writers had hailed as the quintessence of the sublime.

Provenance

W. Lockett Agnew, London
Sir George W. Macalpine, Kt.
The Corporation of Accrington, presented by Sir George W. Macalpine, Kt., 1911.
Anon. Sale: Phillip's, London, June 22, 1970, Lot P.151.

Exhibitions

Royal Academy, 1885, No. 662.
Royal Jubilee Exhibition, Manchester, 1887, No. 175.
The Art and Mind of Victorian England: Paintings from the Forbes Magazine Collection, University Gallery, University of Minnesota, Minneapolis, 1974, No. 33 (reproduced in catalogue).

References

Art Journal, 1885, p. 225.
The Illustrated London News, May 23, 1885, p. 533.
Art Journal, 1887, p. 251.
William MacDonald Sinclair, "The Life and Work of John MacWhirter, RA," *Art Annual: Supplement to the Art Journal,* 1905, pp. 1, 11, 30, reproduced p. 1.

44. J. MacWhirter, *The Track of a Hurricane.*

SIR JOHN EVERETT MILLAIS, PRA

(1829-1896)

In a letter appraising the abilities of the leading personages associated with the Pre-Raphaelite Brotherhood, John Ruskin (1819-1900) described Millais as, "the most acute-intense and unexampled in genius and artistic power" (*Forbes* Magazine Collection). A genius Millais undoubtedly was. He was born in Southampton in June 1829; his parents moved to London from the Isle of Jersey in 1838 to further his artistic training. He won a silver Medal from the Society of Arts in 1839 and entered the Royal Academy Schools a year later at the unprecedented age of eleven. In 1848, two years after he had exhibited his first painting at the Royal Academy, he founded with William Holman Hunt (q.v.), Dante Gabriel Rossetti (1828-1882) and four others the Pre-Raphaelite Brotherhood (see Appendix I). Millais worked strictly in the Pre-Raphaelite manner only until around 1853, the year in which he was made an Associate of the Royal Academy. As late as 1856, however, his pictures were still tightly executed. Starting with *Sir Isumbras at the Ford* of 1857, his work quickly became looser in handling, more sentimental in subject matter, and more popular with the public. This change corresponded so closely to the date of his marriage (to the former Mrs. Ruskin) that it seems likely that there was some connection. Now, he had to provide for his rapidly growing family. In 1863 he was elected a full Academician, in 1885 he was created a baronet, and a few months before his death on August 13, 1896, he was elected President of the Royal Academy. During his career he exhibited one hundred and eighty-nine works there. Exhibitions of his work were held at the Academy in 1898 and again in 1967.

Bibliography

Walter Armstrong, "Sir John Everett Millais Bart., RA: His Life and Work," *Art Annual: Supplement to the Art Journal*, 1885.
Marion H. Spielmann, *Millais and His Works*, London, 1898.
Alfred L. Baldry, *Sir John Everett Millais*, London, 1899.
John Guille Millais, *The Life and Letters of Sir John Everett Millais*, 2 Vols., London, 1899.
Arthur Fish, *John Everett Millais*, New York, 1923.
Mary Bennett, *Sir John Everett Millais*, Royal Academy, London, and Walker Art Gallery, Liverpool, 1967 (exhibition catalogue).

45. *THE ESCAPE OF A HERETIC, 1559

Oil on panel: 10 x 8 inches
Inscribed, lower left: *JEM* (monogram)
Original frame

The Escape of a Heretic, 1559 is a reduced replica of the painting of the same title (Museo de Arte de Ponce, Puerto Rico), which Millais exhibited at the Royal Academy in 1857. The lengthy quotation which was printed in the catalogue explains the incident:

"At Valladolid, this Friday before Good Friday, A.D. 1584, before the Licentiate Cristoval Rodrigues, Commissary of the Holy Inquition, appears Fray Juan Romero, monk of the order of Saint Dominic, in the convent of said order in the said city familiar of the said Holy Inquisition, and having sworn to speak the truth, saith—'That, having been assigned, together with Fray Diego Nuño, familiar of the said Holy Inquisition, as confessor to Maria Juana di Acuna y Villajos, late in close prison of the said Holy Inquisitor, convict, as an obstinate heretic, and left to be delivered to the secular arm at the Act of Faith appointed to be held in the said city, before His Most Catholic Majesty our Lord the King, this day, he was yesterday at noon in the prison of the said prisoner, together with a person unknown, whom he supposed to be the said Fray Diego, but saw not his face by reason of his wearing his hood drawn forward, when he was of a sudden set upon gagged, and bound by the said person unknown, and his habit stripped off and put upon the said prisoner, who so passed out from said prison with the said person unknown, nor hath since been discovered by the deponent or the other familiars of the said Holy Inquisition in the said city.'"

(Documentos relativos á los Procesos por la Inquisicion de Valladolid)

In the same year Millais also exhibited *A Dream of the Past: Sir Isumbras at the Ford* (Lady Lever Art Gallery, Port Sunlight), which he accompanied in the Royal Academy catalogue with some lines of verse purporting to be from a medieval ballad but in fact written for the occasion by Millais's friend the playwright Tom Taylor. It seems likely that the exciting passage supposedly culled from the *"Documentos . . . de Valladolid"* was equally fake. The girl wears a *sambenito,* or penitential garment, of yellow sacking painted with devils roasting souls in flames; a hood made of the same material has been thrown upon the ground. The bound jailor's gag is held in place by his own rosary. The rescuer, although wearing the habit of a monk, is shown to be of another station in life by the bit of

(continued on page 149)

J. E. Millais, *The Escape of a Heretic, 1559*
(Museo de Arte de Ponce, Puerto Rico)

J. E. Millais, *"Mercy": St. Bartholomew's Day, 1572*
(The Tate Gallery, London)

45. J. E. Millais, *The Escape of a Heretic, 1559.*
(see color Plate XVI, p. 174)

46. * FOR THE SQUIRE

Oil on canvas: 34 x 25-3/4 inches
Inscribed, lower right: *JEM* (monogram) *1882*

Millais first exhibited *For the Squire* at the Grosvenor Gallery, rather than at the Royal Academy, but it is analogous in style and subject to pictures which he sent to the Academy. It was included in the exhibition of his works there following his death. It is typical of the sentimental pictures produced by Millais after his Pre-Raphaelite period, especially during the last two decades of his life. Comparable representations of little girls of the same period are *Cherry Ripe* (1879), *Sweet Eyes* (1881), *Pomona* (1882) and *Lilacs* (1886). These pictures, although not Millais's most ambitious works, had great popular success, and many, including *For the Squire*, were engraved. *For the Squire* shows a little damsel shyly proffering a letter to an awe-inspiring but unseen Squire. Although many Victorians would have agreed with the reviewer of the *Magazine of Art* when he wrote in 1883 that, "Mr. Millais is not at his highest in . . . his *For the Squire*," they also would have acknowledged that even at his loosest Millais was still Victorian England's most gifted painter, and that the sugary sweet letter-bearer does have a very convincing presence. It is interesting to note that the brick wall in the background repeats a motif first used by Millais in *The Huguenot* of thirty years earlier.

Provenance

H. F. Makins
The Rt. Hon. Lord Sherfield, G. C. B., by descent (Sale: Christie's, London, July 10, 1970, No. 161, reproduced).

Exhibitions

Grosvenor Gallery, London, 1883, No. 117.
The Works of Sir John E. Millais, Bart., PRA, Grosvenor Gallery, London, 1888, No. 75.
Works by the Late Sir John Everett Millais Bart., PRA, Winter Exhibition, Royal Academy, 1898, No. 240.
On loan to The Metropolitan Museum of Art, New York, February 1973-July, 1974, Loan No. L. 1973. 1. 2.
The Art and Mind of Victorian England: Paintings from the Forbes Magazine Collection, University Gallery, University of Minnesota, Minneapolis, 1974, No. 35 (reproduced in catalogue in color).

References

Magazine of Art, 1883, p. 352.
Marion H. Spielmann, *Millais and His Works*, London, 1898, pp. 122, 179.
John Guille Millais, *The Life and Letters of Sir John Everett Millais*, London, 1899, Vol. II, pp. xi, 481, 495, detail reproduced p. 435.
"Mr. Forbes Adds a Tearjerker", *Evening News*, London, July 10, 1970.
Terence Mullaly, "Ladbrooke Landscape Fetches 3,600 Gns.," *The Daily Telegraph*, London, July 11, 1970.
Christopher Wood, "The Great Victorian Revivial," *Auction*, November, 1970, p. 39.
John Herbert (ed.), *Christie's Review of the Year*, 1969/1970, reproduced p. 67.
Michael Findlay, "Forbes Saves the Queen," *Arts Magazine*, February, 1973, p. 30, reproduced p. 27.
"It's from Forbes!," *Forbes*, November 1, 1973, p. 69, November 15, 1973, p. 121, December 1, 1973, p. 67, reproduced in color in each (advertisement).
"University of Minnesota looks at Victorian era of England," *Free Press*, Mankato, Minnesota, August 26, 1974, reproduced.
"University to have Victorian Festival," *Gazette*, Stillwater, Minnesota, August 27, 1974, reproduced.
Carole Nelson, "Exhibit wins respect for long-neglected Victorian paintings," *St. Paul's Sunday Pioneer Press, Family Life Section*, September 29, 1974, reproduced p. 1.
"A glimpse of Victoria's world," *Minneapolis Tribune*, September 22, 1974, reproduced.

47. A SCENE FROM 'PEVERIL OF THE PEAK'

Oil and watercolor on paper: 35-1/2 x 46 inches
Inscribed, lower right: *J. E. Millais. 1841*
Original frame

This youthful effort was not exhibited at the Royal Academy, or elsewhere, during the artist's lifetime. It was, however, included in the retrospective exhibition of Millais's works held at the Academy after his death. It was executed a year after Millais was admitted to the Royal Academy Schools and is according to J. G. Millais, "the most elaborate work of his early years." The scene was inspired by the forty-third chapter of Sir Walter Scott's *Peveril of the Peak:* "Bridgenorth from the gallery of the chapel, disclosing to Julian's view one of the conventicles which were illegally held in London at the time."

Attached to the back of the picture is the following note:

> This remarkable drawing was made by my brother, Sir John Everett Millais, at the age of 11/12 years. I myself was a school boy at Kings College School and can well remember him at work at it and the great excitement we all felt at home during its execution. I have written this to guarantee the genuineness of this work as it is almost incredible that it should have come from so young a child. (Signed) W. H. Millais.

Provenance

W. H. Millais
Mrs. A. J. Millais, by descent, 1898 (Sale: Christie's, London, July 30, 1924, Lot 123).
The First Lord Leverhulme
Lady Lever Art Gallery, Port Sunlight (Sale: Christie's, London, June 6, 1958, No. 72, 6 gns., unsold).
Fine Art Society, London

Exhibitions

Works by the Late Sir John Everett Millais, Bart, PRA, Winter Exhibition, Royal Academy, 1898, No. 209.
Lady Lever Art Gallery, Port Sunlight, until 1958.
Aspects of Victorian Art, Fine Art Society, London, 1971, No. 115.

References

John Guille Millais, *The Life and Letters of Sir John Everett Millais*, London, 1899, Vol. II, p. 489, reproduced Vol. I, p. 11.
Arthur Fish, *Sir John Everett Millais*, New York, 1923, p. 6.

46. J. E. Millais, *For the Squire.*

47. J. E. Millais, A Scene from *'Peveril of the Peak'.*

109

ALBERT MOORE
(1841-1893)

was born at York in September, 1841, the youngest of fourteen children of a minor landscape and portrait painter William Moore (1790-1851). Four of Moore's older brothers also became painters, the most successful being Henry Moore (q.v.). Moore manifested an extremely precocious talent and began receiving instruction from his father and brothers at an early age. When he was twelve years old, Moore was awarded a medal for one of his drawings by the Department of Science and Art at the York School of Design. In 1855, the family moved to London and two years later, at the age of fifteen, Moore made his debut at the Royal Academy's Summer Exhibition with two watercolors of dead birds. The following spring, he entered the Academy Schools, where he remained only briefly, finding their methods too restrictive. In 1858, he made a visit to northern France with William Eden Nesfield (1835-1888), the architect whose partner was Richard Norman Shaw (1831-1912). Soon afterwards he received, through Nesfield's good offices, a number of decorative mural and ceiling commissions.

During the early 1860s Moore painted in a forceful quasi-Pre-Raphaelite style, turning frequently to the Old Testament for his subjects. From late 1862 until his mother's death in 1863, Moore worked in Rome. Upon his return to England, he was commissioned to work on the decorations of Coombe Abbey, Warwickshire, the house designed by Nesfield for Lord Craven. His fresco of The Four Seasons, exhibited at the Royal Academy in 1864, showed his developing preference for decorative rather than narrative elements in his pictures. Two years later he exhibited his last Old Testament subject (The Shulamite). That year he also began to use the Greek anthemion device as a signature (in a picture titled Apricots) and to give his pictures deliberately ambiguous titles based on some incidental accessory (Apricots shows two girls walking in a garden).

In 1865 The Marble Seat caught the attention of James Abbott McNeill Whistler (1834-1903) and the two became life-long friends. During the latter half of the '60s, in fact, their work developed on very similar lines. Shortly after their first meeting, Whistler wrote to Henri Fantin-Latour (1836-1904) that Moore should replace Alphonse Legros (1837-1911) in their Societé des Trois, and in 1878, Moore repaid the compliment by being the only artist to testify on Whistler's behalf in his libel suit against John Ruskin (1819-1900).

After its opening in 1877, Moore became a frequent contributor to the annual exhibitions of the Grosvenor Gallery, although he continued to show at the Royal Academy. In 1884, he was elected an associate of the Royal Water-Colour Society; his temperament denied him similar recognition from other institutions. In 1890-91, a tumor developed in Moore's thigh, and despite several periods of improvement in his condition, he died on September 25, 1893, having exhibited forty-two pictures at the annual exhibitions of the Royal Academy.

Bibliography

Art Journal, 1893, pp. 334-335 (obituary)
Alfred L. Baldry, Albert Moore, His Life and Works, London 1894.
Richard Green, Albert Moore and his Contemporaries, Laing Art Gallery, Newcastle-upon-Tyne, 1972 (exhibition catalogue).

48. * A FLOWER WALK

Oil on canvas: 10-3/4 x 4-1/4 inches
Inscribed, lower left, with anthemion
Original frame

This picture has been identified as a smaller version of the work of the same title which Moore exhibited at the Royal Academy in 1875. According to the standard monograph on Moore by Alfred Lys Baldry, the exhibited painting was the same height as this picture, but two inches wider. However, as Baldry's catalogue of Moore's works lists only the exhibited version of A Flower Walk, and as this is the only version known, it is possible that Baldry could have made a slight mistake in his measurements and that this picture was the exhibited one. The figure standing in profile with her head turned looking out of the picture is based loosely on one of the figures in Moore's Apricots exhibited in 1866.

At the Academy A Flower Walk was hung with two other small works by Moore, A Palm Fan and Pansies. Despite their diminutive size, the pictures attracted a considerable amount of critical attention. After giving brief descriptions of each, the reviewer for The Illustrated London News enthused,

> From these pictures, small as they are, we derive a vastly higher idea of the artist's powers than from the large works which preceded them. This is decorative painting of the rarest and most artistic. The pure classical feeling, the faultless draughtsmanship, modelling . . . above all the original and lovely colouring, are deserving of the warmest praise. . . . The sparing piquant addition of positive colour sprinkled with an unerring colourist instinct such as could not be surpassed in the best Japanese art, yield as purer aesthetic pleasure than anything of the same or similar aim

in the exhibition; indeed, there is nothing that can be compared to them (May 15, 1875, pp. 470-471).

Ruskin was no less enthusiastic in his Notes on the 1875 Academy exhibition:

> It is well worthwhile to go straight . . . to the two small studies by Mr. Albert Moore, 356 [A Flower Walk] and 357 [Pansies], which are consumately artistic and scientific work. Examine them closely and with patience. . . . Or try the effect of concealing the yellow flower in the hair, in the Flower Walk. And for comparison with the elementary method of M. Tadema [q.v.], look at the blue reflection on the chin in his figure; at its right arm. . . . And you ought afterwards, if you have an eye for colour, never more to mistake a tinted drawing for a painting (Works, Vol. XIV, pp. 272-273).

Provenance

Anon. Sale: Sotheby's Belgravia, London, November 20, 1973, Lot 52.
Fine Art Society, London (Agents).

Exhibitions

Royal Academy, 1875, No. 356 (?).

References

Art Journal, 1875, p. 247 (?).
Henry Blackburn, Academy Notes, London, 1875, pp. 27-28 (?).
The Illustrated London News, May 15, 1875, pp. 470-471 (?).
John Ruskin, "Notes on Some of the Principal Pictures Exhibited in the Rooms of the Royal Academy: 1875" (reprinted in Works, Vol. XIV, pp. 272-273, edited by E. J. Cook and Alexander Wedderburn, London, 1903-1912 -?).
Alfred L. Baldry, Albert Moore, His Life and Works, London, 1894, pp. 44, 94-95, 103 (gives dimensions as 10-1/4 x 6-1/4 inches -?).

48. A. Moore, *A Flower Walk*.
(*see color Plate XVII, p. 175*)

HENRY MOORE, RA

(1831-1895)

the older brother of Albert Moore (q.v.), was born at York on March 7, 1831. He studied first with his father and eventually attended the York School of Design. In 1853 he was admitted as a student to the Royal Academy Schools and, in that same year, exhibited his first work, a landscape entitled *Glen Clunie, Castletown of Braemar, Aberdeen,* at the Academy. This was followed by one hundred and fifteen more exhibits before the artist's death on June 22, 1895. Almost all of these were either landscapes or, more especially, seascapes. Although by the mid-Seventies he was considered one of "the most original artists of these times," it was not until after the Chantrey Bequest purchased his *Cat's Paws off the Land* in 1885 that he was elected an Associate of the Royal Academy. He did not attain full Academic Honors until 1893, two years before his death.

In 1891 he was almost killed when he fell off a bus, but after a long and painful recovery he was able to resume painting. The quality of his work was not affected, and the author of his obituary in the *Art Journal* described his death as coming "at the very summit of his power, before any sign of failure from age or weakened health had had a chance of appearing in his work."

Bibliography

Lionel G. Robinson, "Henry and Albert Moore," *Art Journal,* 1881, pp. 161-164.
Art Journal, 1895, p. 280 (obituary).
Frank Maclean, *Henry Moore, RA,* London, 1905.

subject worthy of the artist's attention" (Maclean, p. 151). This preoccupation with just the sea itself gives Moore's late seascapes a certain repetitiveness. His constant representations of vast expanses of ocean under different weather conditions have only the sparest specific literal reference points to keep them from appearing to be part of a series of variations upon a single theme, like Monet's series of the same subject under different light conditions. Only the little sail boat on the horizon makes it possible to differentiate *Half a Gale: Outside Poole* from several other seascapes by Moore until one has studied the quality of the waves carefully.

Provenance

Charles Winn, Birmingham
Arthur Tooth & Sons, Ltd., London
Anon. Sale: Christie's, London, November 20, 1970, Lot 264.

Exhibitions

Winter Exhibition, Royal Academy, 1903, No. 155.
The Art and Mind of Victorian England: Paintings from the Forbes Magazine Collection, University Gallery, University of Minnesota, Minneapolis, 1974, No. 36 (reproduced in catalogue).

References

Frank Maclean, *Henry Moore, RA,* London, 1905, pp. xvi, 198, reproduced opposite p. 152.
Peter Altman, "Victorian age ideals evident in art works," *The Minneapolis Star,* September 28, 1974.

49. HALF A GALE: OUTSIDE POOLE

Oil on canvas: 26 x 40 inches
Inscibed, lower left: *H. Moore. 1892.*
Original frame

This painting was not exhibited at the Royal Academy in an annual Summer Exhibition, but it appeared there in a loan exhibition two years after Queen Victoria's death. In his book on Henry Moore, Frank Maclean gives the following description of *Half a Gale: Outside Poole:* "Choppy, bright blue sea, and sky slightly clouded. Excellent wave drawing, and the play of light on the surface of the water is remarkable. Very crisp in the handling. A sailing boat is seen on the horizon."

Ships and sailors were of secondary interest to Moore. He was a pioneer in his willingness to "regard the sea, by itself and for itself, as a

49. H. Moore, *Half a Gale: Outside Poole.*

HENRY NELSON O'NEIL, ARA

(1817-1880)

was born of English parents in Czarist St. Petersburg in 1817. He was brought to England at the age of six and eventually was allowed to enter the Royal Academy Schools.

In 1837, the year of Queen Victoria's accession, he and several fellow students banded together in a group called The Clique (see Appendix I). According to John Imray, O'Neil's ambition at this time was to paint "Incidents of striking character appealing to the feelings." O'Neil was elected an Associate of the Royal Academy in 1860, after he achieved great acclaim with his entry of 1858, a work entitled *Eastward Ho! August 1857*, and its sequel entitled *Home Again, 1858*, exhibited the following year. In 1864 his *Purity* was the subject of a small article in the *Art Journal*, in which the writer concluded that the artist was "On the high road to ultimate distinction which, in part at least, he has already won." However, O'Neil never achieved the rank of full Academician, despite the ninety-seven works he exhibited at the Academy.

In the 1860s, besides *Purity* his only works to attract much attention were *The Landing at Gravesend of the Princess Alexandra of Denmark* (1864), *The Lay of King Canute* (1865) and *The Last Moments of Raffaele* (1866). The latter was considered "his work of highest character." O'Neil never again, however, equaled *Eastward Ho! August 1857* in popularity and his later works, according to the *Art Journal* "did not make the prominent impression they at one time promised to do."

During his later years he devoted much of his time to writing and music, and perhaps the decline of his work can be attributed to his increased interest in other fields. Although he never fulfilled his expectations as an artist, his obituary in *The Times* was written by Anthony Trollope. The writer was portrayed in O'Neil's *Billiards at the Garrick* of 1869, and he fondly wrote of the artist as "one who was simple, just and affectionate as a child."

Bibliography

Art Journal, 1880, p. 171 (obituary).
John Imray, "A Reminiscence of Sixty Years Ago," *Art Journal*, 1898, p. 202.
Derek Hudson, "Billiards at the Garrick in 1869," *Connoisseur*, December, 1969, p. 274.

50. * EASTWARD HO! AUGUST 1857; HOME AGAIN — 1858

Oil on canvas, framed to appear as a pair:
20-3/4 x 35 inches
Inscribed, lower right on *Eastward Ho!:*
H. O'Neil
Original slip frame

These two pictures painted on one canvas are replicas of details from two different works, *Eastward Ho! August 1857* (Collection Sir Richard Proby, Bt.) and *Home Again — 1858* (Private Collection, Great Britain), which O'Neil exhibited at the Royal Academy in 1858 and 1859 respectively. *Eastward Ho!* was one of the pictures of the year in 1857. The scene depicted in the canvas shows troops departing for the Indian Mutiny saying their farewells. Its popularity caused O'Neil to paint a sequel showing the troops returning. This was only slightly less popular than its predecessor, and O'Neil executed a number of replicas of both. The canvas catalogued here is decidedly the most unusual of these. It shows the most touching incident from each canvas: the same family is seen, first, at the sad moment of separation and, secondly, at the moving moment of reunion a year later. Another replica of these two details is in a private collection in England.

Provenance

Anon. Sale: Sotheby's, London, May 20, 1970, Lot 48.

Exhibitions

Victorian Art, The Emily Lowe Gallery, Hofstra University, Hempstead, New York, 1972, Nos. 83 and 84 (*Eastward Ho! August 1857* reproduced).
The Art and Mind of Victorian England: Paintings from the Forbes Magazine Collection, University Gallery, University of Minnesota, Minneapolis, 1974, No. 37 (both reproduced in catalogue, *Eastward Ho! August 1857* in color).

References

Graham Reynolds, *Victorian Painting*, London, 1966, p. 87.
Melvin Waldfogel, "Introduction," *The Art and Mind of Victorian England: Paintings from the Forbes Magazine Collection,* University Gallery, University of Minnesota, Minneapolis, 1974, pp. 19, 22 (exhibition catalogue).
"A glimpse of Victoria's world," *Minneapolis Tribune,* September 22, 1974, *Eastward Ho! August 1857* reproduced.
Peter Altman, "Victorian age ideals evident in art works," *The Minneapolis Star,* September 28, 1974.
Lyndel King, "Heroism began at home," *Art News,* November, 1974, p. 45.
"Victorian Art and Mind," *Apollo,* December, 1974, p. 527, both reproduced p. 527.

Eastward Ho! August 1857
(Collection Sir Richard Proby)

Home Again — 1858

50. H. N. O'Neil, *Eastward Ho! August 1857; Home Again —*
1858.
(see color Plates XVIII and XIX, pp. 176-177)

SIR WILLIAM QUILLER ORCHARDSON, RA

(1832-1910)

was the son of Abraham Orchardson, a tailor. He was born in Edinburgh on March 27, 1832, and entered the Trustees' Academy in that city when he was only thirteen. There he studied under the painter John Ballantyne (1815-1897). He continued to attend classes until 1855 so as to be able to study with Robert Scott Lauder (1803-1862) who came to the Academy in 1852. Between 1855 and 1862 he worked in Edinburgh and began to add literary themes to his repertoire. His favorite authors were Shakespeare, Scott, Dickens, and Keats; he also painted at least one subject from Harriet Beecher Stowe (*Uncle Tom and Little Eva*, c. 1865). He continued to paint literary scenes after his arrival in London in 1862. The following year he exhibited the first of some one hundred and seven pictures he was to eventually show at the Royal Academy.

In 1870 he visited Venice with Frederick Walker (1840-1875). The latter persuaded Orchardson to do some open-air sketching but this experience does not seem to have had any lasting effect on his work. Two years before going to Venice, Orchardson had been elected an Associate of the Royal Academy. In 1877 he was elevated to full membership.

Now that he was completely "established," Orchardson turned his talents to contemporary genre subjects. The most famous of these are his psychological dramas of upper-class life such as *The First Cloud* (National Gallery of Victoria, Melbourne), *Mariage de Convenance* (Glasgow Art Gallery), and its sequel, *Mariage de Convenance—After* (Aberdeen Art Gallery). In 1907 Orchardson was knighted by King Edward VII. A self-made man, he was paranoid about losing his eyesight and thus his livelihood. He never did lose his vision, however, and he died peaceful and prosperous in London on April 13, 1910.

Bibliography

James Dafforne, "British Artists: Their Style and Character; No. XCIII—W. Q. Orchardson," *Art Journal*, 1870, pp. 233-235.
Alice Meynell, "William Quiller Orchardson," *Magazine of Art*, Vol. IV, 1881, pp. 276-281.
Walter Armstrong, *The Art of William Quiller Orchardson, Portfolio*, February, 1895 (No. 14 in a series of monthly monographs).
James Stanley Little, "The Life and Work of William Q. Orchardson, RA," *Art Annual: Supplement to the Art Journal*, 1897.
James L. Caw, *Scottish Painting, Past and Present 1620-1908*, Edinburgh, 1908, pp. 236-240.
Hilda Orchardson Gray, *The Life of William Quiller Orchardson, RA, DCL, HRSA, PSPP*, London, 1930.
William R. Hardie, *Sir William Quiller Orchardson, RA*, The Scottish Arts Council, Edinburgh, 1972 (exhibition catalogue).

51. * "THE QUEEN OF THE SWORDS"

Oil on canvas: 33-1/4 x 53 inches
Inscribed, lower left: *W Q Orchardson-/77*

The inspiration for *"The Queen of the Swords"* was a passage from *The Pirate* by Sir Walter Scott:

> A dozen cutlasses, selected hastily from an old arm-chest, and whose rusted hue bespoke how seldom they left the sheath, armed the same number of young Zetlanders, with whom mingled six maidens, led by Minna Troil; and the minstrelsy instantly commenced a tune appropriate to the ancient Norwegian war-dance, the evolutions of which are perhaps still practiced in those remote islands.
>
> The first movement of the dance was graceful and majestic, the youths holding their swords erect, and without much gesture but the tune, and the corresponding motion of the dancers, became gradually more and more rapid—they clashed their swords together, in measured time, with a spirit which gave the exercise a dangerous appearance in the eye of the spectator, through the firmness, justice, and accuracy with which the dancers kept time with the stroke of their weapons, did, in truth, ensure its safety. The most singular part of the exhibition was the courage exhibited by the female performers, who now, surrounded by the swordsmen, seemed like the Sabine maidens in the hands of their Roman lovers; now moving under the arch of steel which the young men had formed, by crossing their weapons over the heads of their fair partners, resembled the band of Amazons when they first joined in the Pyrrhic dance with the followers of Theseus. But by far the most striking and appropriate figure was that of Minna Troil, whom Halcro had long since entitled the Queen of Swords, and who, indeed, moved amidst the swordsmen with an air, which seemed to hold all the drawn blades as the proper accompaniments of her person, and the implements of her pleasure. And when the mazes of the dance became more intricate, when the close and continuous clash of the weapons made some of her companions shrink, and show signs of fear, her cheek, her lip, and her eye, seemed rather to announce, that, at the moment when the weapons flashed fastest, and rung sharpest around her, she was most completely self-possessed, and in her element.

This scene as described by Scott is, however, considerably less refined than the elegant gathering presented by Orchardson. The artist has, in fact, transposed the subject from Scott's rude war-dance set in the remote Shetland

(continued on page 150)

W. Q. Orchardson, *"Minna Troil"*
study for *"The Queen of the Swords"*
(National Galleries of Scotland)

W. Q. Orchardson, *"The Queen of the Swords"*—sketch
(National Galleries of Scotland)

W. Q. Orchardson,
reduced replica *"The Queen of the Swords"*
(National Galleries of Scotland)

51. W. Q. Orchardson, *"The Queen of the Swords."*
(*see color Plate XX, p. 178*)

JOHN PHILLIP, RA

(1817-1867)

was born in Aberdeen on April 13, 1817, the son of a shoemaker. He was apprenticed to a house painter named Anderson and later worked in the studio of a local portrait painter James Forbes. In 1834 he made his way to London as a stowaway on the brig *Manly*. Despite his previous experience he had never considered becoming an artist until after spending a day at the Royal Academy exhibition. This experience determined him on pursuing a career in art. Two years later, the generosity of Lord Panmure enabled him to further his desires. With his Lordship's gift of £50, he studied first under a genre painter, Thomas Musgrove Joy (1812-1866), and then entered the Royal Academy Schools. There in 1837 he joined together with some fellow students to form the group called The Clique (see Appendix I). According to a friend, Phillip's individual aim at this time was to paint "incidents in the lives of famous persons." He first exhibited at the Royal Academy in 1838. From 1839 to 1846 he worked in Aberdeen, but continued to send pictures to the Academy's shows.

Around 1846 Phillip married the sister of the painter Richard Dadd (1817-1866), who had been one of his fellow members of The Clique. She, like her brother, lost her reason and had to be confined to a mental hospital. Her breakdown was possibly the reason why, in 1851, Phillip made his first trip to Spain. Prior to this his *oeuvre* consisted of portraits and scenes of humble Scottish life. After the Spanish tour and subsequent stays in 1856 and 1860, he devoted himself to recording Spanish customs and history on canvas. This preoccupation earned him the nickname "Spanish" Phillip.

He became an Associate member of the Royal Academy in 1857 and a full Academician in 1859. Before his premature death on February 27, 1867, he exhibited fifty-five works there.

Bibliography

Art Journal, 1867, p. 127 (obituary).
Allan Cunningham, *Lives of the Most Eminent British Painters*, London, 1879-1880, Vol. III, pp. 434-445, (revised edition, annotated and continued to the present time by Mrs. Charles Heaton).
Walter Armstrong, *Scottish Painters*, London, 1888, pp. 57-62.
James Dafforne, *Pictures by John Phillip*, London, n.d.
William D. McKay, *The Scottish School of Painting*, London, 1906, pp. 278-293.
James L. Caw, *Scottish Painting, Past and Present 1620-1908*, Edinburgh, 1908, pp. 179-184.
Charles Carter, *John Phillip, RA*, Aberdeen Art Gallery, Aberdeen, 1967 (exhibition catalogue).
Patricia Allderidge, *The Late Richard Dadd*, Tate Gallery, London, 1974, pp. 13, 15, 44 (exhibition catalogue).

52. * THE EARLY CAREER OF MURILLO, 1634

Oil on canvas: 72 x 100 inches
Inscribed, lower left: *JP* (monogram) *1865*, center middle: *B. E. Murillo 1634*
Original frame

The Early Career of Murillo, 1634 was greeted with almost unparalleled critical acclaim when it appeared at the Royal Academy in 1865. The reviewer for the *Art Journal* devoted almost one thousand words praising and describing the picture. Among his observations were: "Last year in *La Gloria* [Phillip] surpassed himself; in this year's exhibition, he has outtopped his highest triumph," and: "Mr. Phillip, in a city he has made his own, has seized upon a subject which, for national character, local colour, and historic truth, is not to be surpassed." Only Francis Turner Palgrave writing in his *Essays on Art* had expressed reservations. He doubted that it would be "rated quite so highly when its first charm has passed." Almost thirty years later, R. A. M. Stevenson, a critic whose tastes had been formed by French *plein-air* painting, writing in the *Art Journal* confirmed Palgrave's prediction:

> Connoisseurs examine a canvas by Murillo in the open-air, or at least in Phillip's open-air, which is scarcely the same thing. The picture is composed well in the old piled-up style, and painted from sketches made at all sorts of different focuses. It places us at the back of Murillo's canvas; the handling and realization are powerful but not consistent, the general effect is unconvincing and the colour is plentiful but not rich.

The inspiration for the scene came from Sir William Stirling-Maxwell's *Annals of the Artists of Spain*, a passage from which is quoted in the 1865 Royal Academy catalogue:

> He was reduced to earn his daily bread by painting coarse and hasty pictures for the Feria [weekly fair], held in broad street branching from the northern end of the Old Alameda, and in front of the old church of 'All Saints,' remarkable for its picturesque semi-Moorish belfry. This venerable market presents every Thursday an aspect which has changed but little since the days of Murillo. Fruit, vegetables, and coarse pottery, old clothes, old iron, still cover the ground or load the stalls as they did two centuries ago, when the unknown youth stood among the gipsies, muleteers, and mendicant friars, selling for a few reals those productions of his early pencil, for which royal collectors are now ready to contend.

Although the picture on the young artist's easel is identifiable as Murillo's *St. John and the Lamb*

(National Gallery, London), and hence as a religious subject, the side of Murillo's career which would have had greatest appeal to a Victorian artist such as Phillip would have been his genre pictures. Phillip's earliest successes were Scottish genre subjects in the tradition of Wilkie (q.v. — who it is worth noting was also attracted by Spain; see No. 69), and he depicted Spain in similar genre terms. Although the subject of the picture is drawn from the past, only Murillo and one or two subordinate figures wear recognizably seventeenth-century costume. As the quotation from Stirling-Maxwell indicates, this market scene in Seville "has changed but little since the days of Murillo." The theme of the artist in contact with and drawing sustenance from real life has an obvious relevance to the growing popularity of subjects from everyday life in mid-nineteenth-century painting:

A second version of this picture dated 1866 was lent by C. P. Matthews to the *London International Exhibition* of 1873 (No. 1218).

Provenance

Henry McConnel (Sale: Christie's, London, March 27, 1886, Lot 80, £3,990).
James M. Keiller, Dundee (Sale: Christie's, London, May 25, 1895, Lot 94).
Sir J. B. Robinson (Sale: Christie's, London, June 6, 1923, Lot 116, £1,890).
Anon. Sale: Christie's, London, October 21, 1970, Lot 53.
Thomas Agnew & Sons, London (Agents).

Exhibitions

Royal Academy, 1865, No. 156.
London International Exhibition, 1873, No. 1329.
Royal Jubilee Exhibition, Manchester, 1887, No. 595.
Winter Exhibition, Royal Academy, 1894, No. 11.

References

Art Journal, 1865, pp. 161-172.
Athenaeum, April 27, 1865, pp. 591-593.
The Times, April 29, 1865, p. 12.
The Illustrated London News, May 6, 1865, p. 439.
"Private View of the Royal Academy," *Punch*, May 13, 1865, pp. 196-197.
The Reader, May 20, 1865, pp. 579-580.
Francis Turner Palgrave, "The Royal Academy of 1865," *Essays on Art*, New York, 1867, pp. 110-111.
Allan Cunningham, *Lives of the Most Eminent British Painters*, London, 1879-80, Vol. III, pp. 442-443 (revised edition, annotated and continued to the present time by Mrs. Heaton).
Walter Armstrong, *Scottish Painters*, London, 1888, p. 58.
Walter Armstrong, *Celebrated Pictures exhibited at the Manchester Royal Jubilee Exhibition*, London, 1888, p. 2.
Robert Brydall, *Art in Scotland: Its Origin and Progress*, Edinburgh and London, 1889, p. 452.

(continued on page 150)

52. J. Phillip, *The Early Career of Murillo, 1634.*
(*see color Plate XXI, p. 179*)

LASLETT JOHN POTT
(1837-1898)

had a talent bordering on genius as a child, but he never lived up to the expectations engendered by his early skill. He was born in Newark, Nottinghamshire, in 1837 and at the age of five is recorded as having produced very credible hunting scenes and marine views. At the age of sixteen his father caused him to be articled to an architect. This proved unsatisfactory for both parties, and young Pott was allowed to enroll in Carey's Art School in London. He completed his studies as a pupil of the Scottish painter Alexander Johnstone (1815-1891) and first exhibited at the Royal Academy in 1860. His *Puss in Boots—Behind the Scenes* (see No. 53), exhibited in 1863, won him a modicum of popular attention. In the early 1870s he was considered by some critics to be an up-and-coming artist, but after a few initial successes, his pictures failed to attract much notice. Between 1860 and 1897 Pott exhibited some forty-three works at the Royal Academy, but he was never elected even an Associate member of the institution. When he died on the first of August, 1898, he was accorded only a two line obituary in the *Magazine of Art* (Vol. XXII, p. 632).

Bibliography

James Dafforne, "The Works of Laslett John Pott," *Art Journal,* 1877, pp. 257-260.

53. PUSS IN BOOTS— BEHIND THE SCENES

Oil on canvas: 24 x 18 inches

Puss in Boots—Behind the Scenes was Pott's first "success" as an artist. When it was exhibited at the Royal Academy in 1863, it was hung on "the line," a distinction which, according to the reviewer for the *Art Journal*, the picture "although of no very exceptional merit" had "fairly won." The critic for *The Reader* went on at greater length and with more enthusiasm.

> Mr. Pott's subject from the back scenes of the stage . . . may be founded on observation. Probably it is; for there is something sad and always touching in sacrificing the innocency of children on the altar of theatrical necessity. . . . The picture is a very clever one, and the subject has not been vulgarized as it infallibly would have been in the hands of any but a reflecting man.

In his biographical article about Pott, James Dafforne gives a description of the painting:

> The scene gives to the spectator a peep among the properties of a Christmas pantomime: the clown gossiping with Columbine between the slips, and a man putting the mask of a gigantic pussycat on the head of a little child—an incident from which, as may be assumed, the composition takes its name.

Although seen here in a theatrical transformation, *Puss in Boots* was originally a fairy tale by Charles Perrault (1628-1703) in which a poor miller's son is made rich by the cleverness of his loyal cat.

Provenance

Anon Sale: Sotheby's Belgravia, London, July 10, 1973, Lot 54, reproduced.
Fine Art Society, London (Agents).

Exhibitions

Royal Academy, 1863, No. 434.

References

Art Journal, 1863, p. 111.
The Reader, July 4, 1863, p. 19.
James Dafforne, "The Works of Laslett John Pott," *Art Journal,* 1877, p. 256.
Clara Clement and Lawrence Hutton, *Artists of the Nineteenth Century,* London, 1879, p. 188.

54. FIRE AT A THEATRE

Oil on canvas: 25-1/2 x 36-1/4 inches
Inscribed, lower left: *Laslett J. Pott*

Fire at a Theatre was the second picture using a theatrical setting as a foil exhibited by Pott at the Royal Academy. The drama portrayed, however, is closer to *The Rescue* (National Gallery of Victoria, Melbourne), exhibited in 1855 by Millais (q.v.) than to Pott's own *Puss in Boots—Behind the Scenes* (see No. 53). The composition although horizontal rather than vertical draws heavily on Millais's popular picture of fourteen years earlier. The subject of a rescuer bearing a child out of the flames and into the outstretched arms of a relieved and grateful mother is quite similar to that of the Millais. What gives the Pott its originality is its setting. The extraordinary costumes which give the real drama an air of comic unreality inspired the other title by which the picture has sometimes been known: *Comedy and Tragedy.*

Critics were mixed in their reactions to the picture. In *The Illustrated London News*, the reviewer decided that the picture "vividly realizes a scene of terror, and with much intensity of expression in the pantomimic actors." He went on, however, that "the painting . . . is much coarser than in previous works." The critic for the *Art Journal* acknowledged that "the fool who rushes out from the flame with a child in his arms is greatly admired; and certainly the mother, herself one of the theatric company, frantic with joy at the rescue of her little child, is a fine piece not of acting but of nature." This writer too, however, ends on a less flattering note: "Still, the picture is almost over-much stagey, blazey and violent to be quite agreeable to quiet and refined taste."

Provenance

Leva Gallery, London

Exhibitions

Royal Academy, 1869, No. 2.

References

Art Journal, 1869, p. 162.
The Illustrated London News, May 22, 1869, p. 526.
"After a Visit to the Academy," *Punch,* May 22, 1869, p. 215.
James Dafforne, "The Works of Laslett John Pott," *Art Journal,* 1877, p. 258.
Clara Clement and Lawrence Hutton, *Artists of the Nineteenth Century,* London, 1879, p. 189.

55. * ON THE MARCH FROM MOSCOW

Oil on canvas: 31-3/4 x 47-3/4 inches
Inscribed, lower left: *Laslett J. Pott—1873*

The subject is an imagined moment in the retreat of Napoleon I's armies across the frozen wastes of Russia in 1812. Themes such as this, inspired by Napoleonic history, were popular with artist and public alike throughout the Victorian era. *On the March from Moscow* was the first of several pictures of Napoleonic episodes exhibited by Pott at the Royal Academy, and it received fairly favorable reviews. The critic (continued on page 150)

J. E. Millais, *The Rescue*
(National Gallery of Victoria, Melbourne)

53. L. J. Pott, *Puss in Boots — Behind the Scenes.*

54. L. J. Pott, *Fire at a Theatre.*

55. L. J. Pott, *On the March from Moscow.*

SIR EDWARD JOHN POYNTER, PRA

(1836-1919)

was born in Paris on March 20, 1836. His father was an English architect, Ambrose Poynter, and his mother was the granddaughter of the sculptor Thomas Banks (1735-1805). A boy of delicate health, he had to be removed from the Westminster School and sent to Brighton College in 1849 to take advantage of the more beneficial climate. In 1852 he was taken from Grammar School at Ipswich and sent to Madeira for the same reason. It was in Madeira that he acquired a taste for sketching, and while on holiday in Rome in 1853, he met Frederic Leighton (q.v.), who was six years his senior. The latter was then at work on his *Cimabue's Celebrated Madonna*. Poynter's experience with Leighton seems to have determined him to become an artist, and upon his return to London, he studied first at Leigh's Academy on Newman Street and then at the Royal Academy Schools. He visited the Paris *Exposition* of 1855 and through a distant uncle was able to arrange to become a student of Charles Gleyre (1806-1874), one of France's leading academic artists. He remained in Gleyre's studio for three years; among his fellow students were George Du Maurier (1834-1896) and James Abbott McNeill Whistler (1834-1903). In 1861 he made his debut at the Royal Academy's exhibition with a work entitled *Alla Veneziana*. Four years later he enjoyed his first major success with the dramatic *Faithful unto Death* (City Art Gallery, Manchester), a depiction of the heroism of a Roman sentinel who remained at his post until engulfed in lava during the destruction of Pompeii. In 1867, he scored an even larger success with his colossal *Israel in Egypt*. Two years later he became an Associate of the Royal Academy and seven years after that, a full Academician. In 1896 he succeeded John Everett Millais (q.v.) as President of the Academy. He was knighted shortly thereafter. He filled his Academy post until declining health forced him to resign in 1918. From 1894 to 1906 he also served as Director of the National Gallery. He died on July 26, 1919 having exhibited one hundred and seventy-five works at the Academy during his lifetime.

Bibliography

William Cosmo Monkhouse, "Sir Edward J. Poynter, PRA: His Life and Work," *Art Annual: Supplement to the Art Journal*, 1897.
Malcolm Bell, *The Drawings of Sir E. J. Poynter*, London, 1906.
Connoisseur, September, 1919, pp. 52-53 (obituary).

56. *THE PRODIGAL'S RETURN

Oil on canvas: 47 x 36 inches
Inscribed, lower right: *EJP* (monogram) *1869*

The Prodigal's Return was one of two works based on the parable of the Prodigal Son to be exhibited at the Royal Academy in 1869. Paul Falconer Poole (1807-1879) was the painter of the other, and his *Prodigal Son*, while favorably received, did not share the critical success enjoyed by the work created by Poynter, who was almost thirty years younger and had just been elected an Associate Academician. *The Illustrated London News* devoted a full page to an engraving of Poynter's *Prodigal's Return*. The reviewer went on to praise it thus:

> One feature of Mr. Poynter's treatment . . . must be felt and acknowledged to be strikingly pathetic and therefore successful. That feature is the turning aside the head of the prodigal. . . . So much shame and contrition, so many recollections of truest affection abused and betrayed . . . further comment, apology, or illustration from our pen would be an impertinence.

The same writer, prior to lyricizing on the Prodigal's expression, devoted over one hundred words to attacking the type of realism practised by William Holman Hunt (q.v.) and encouraged in the writings of John Ruskin (1819-1900):

> Some highly respectable persons are very likely, by plausible theories and partisan propagandists, brought to believe that . . . this promising young painter . . . has [not] any right whatever to attempt to deal with the oft painted episode before us, without having previously informed himself of the precise shape, measurement, pattern and material, if not also the market price of the textile fabrics made up into the *abbah*, the under garments, and the *potah*. . . . It is true one may read this and every other great lesson of love and mercy in the sacred pages without being informed of such particulars.

The critic for the *Art Journal* engaged in no polemics, but rather spent the better part of a column comparing Poynter's and Poole's efforts. Turning to Poynter, he made the following observations:

> This . . . is not unlike the manner of Mr. Dyce [q.v.], yet considerably more near to nature. . . . Mr. Poynter has been recently to Italy and we are glad to recognize the influence of Italian schools upon his pictures. . . . under the spell of Venetian colour have Mr. Poynter's pictures lost hardness and gained warm and pleasing harmony.

Provenance

Anon. Sale: Christie's, London, July 14, 1972, Lot 107, reproduced.
Fine Art Society, London (Agents).

Exhibitions

Royal Academy, 1869, No. 110.
The Art and Mind of Victorian England: Paintings from the Forbes Magazine Collection, University Gallery, University of Minnesota, Minneapolis, 1974, No. 39 (reproduced in catalogue).

References

Art Journal, 1869, p. 166.
The Illustrated London News: Special Art Supplement, May 8, 1869, pp. 469, 484, reproduced p. 477.
Frederick G. Stephens, *Artists at Home*, New York, 1884, p. 79.
Herbert Sharp, "A Short Account of the Work of Edward John Poynter, RA," *Studio*, Vol. VII, February 1896, p. 8.
Cosmo Monkhouse, "Sir Edward J. Poynter, PRA: His Life and Work," *Art Annual: Supplement to the Art Journal*, 1897, p. 14, 32.
Richard Hislop (ed.), "The Pre-Raphaelites and Other Painters," *The Art Investment Guide*, Autumn, 1973, p. 2.
Peter Altman, "Victorian age ideals evident in art works," *The Minneapolis Star*, September 28, 1974.
David L. Shirey, "A Major Art Collector at 24," *The New York Times*, January 5, 1974, reproduced p. 17.

Forthcoming References

George Landow, "There began to be a great talking about the Fine Arts," University of Minnesota Lecture Series (to be published in 1975).

56. E. J. Poynter, *The Prodigal's Return.*
(see color Plate XXII, p. 180)

RICHARD REDGRAVE, RA
(1804-1888)

was born on April 30, 1804 in London. His father was an engineer, and he studied with him before he entered the Royal Academy Schools in 1826. A year earlier, he made his Academy debut with *River Brent Near Hanwell*. His early works were mostly confined to landscapes and eighteenth-century costume pieces, executed after the manner of Charles Robert Leslie (q.v.). In the 1840s he pioneered modern genre with such pictures of social comment as *The Sempstress* (see No. 57), *Bad News from Sea*, and *The Poor Teacher*. He became an Associate of the Royal Academy in 1840 and a full Member in 1857. He stopped exhibiting in 1883, by which date he had shown some one hundred and forty-one works at the Academy. He also exhibited at the British Institution and the Society of British Artists. During the last half of his career, his painting was curtailed by his many official duties: he was Keeper of Painting at the South Kensington Museum, Inspector of the Queen's Pictures, and he worked on the national art education project. With his brother Samuel, he wrote *A Century of Painters of the English School*, which was first published in 1866. These duties and projects left him only the summers to paint, and he devoted most of this time to landscapes which he executed in a dry, detailed, quasi-Pre-Raphaelite style.

Bibliography

Richard Redgrave, "Autobiography of Richard Redgrave, ARA," *Art Journal*, 1850, pp. 48-49.

James Dafforne, "British Artists: Their Style and Character; No. XLV—Richard Redgrave, RA," *Art Journal*, 1859, pp. 205-207.

F. M. Redgrave, *Richard Redgrave, CB, RA: A Memoir Compiled from His Diary*, London, 1891.

57. * THE SEMPSTRESS

Oil on canvas: 25 x 30 inches
Inscribed, lower left: *R. Redgrave 1846*
Original frame

Signed and dated 1846, this picture is apparently a later replica of the picture exhibited by Redgrave at the Royal Academy two years before. The location of the earlier work is not known.

Richard Redgrave was a pioneer painter of pictures of contemporary social comment. His earliest efforts in this direction such as *The Reduced Gentleman's Daughter*, exhibited in 1839 and based upon a passage from *The Rambler* by Samuel Johnson, were clothed in the costume of other periods. In 1843 he took the daring step of painting *The Poor Teacher* in

contemporary dress. The result was a moving picture which was surprisingly well-received. Redgrave was commissioned to paint three additional versions of it, including one for John Sheepshanks (Victoria and Albert Museum). This distinguished collector, however, objected to the loneliness of the impoverished young teacher and asked the artist to add some children to the background, a request the artist accommodated. Encouraged by the success of *The Poor Teacher*, Redgrave exhibited *The Sempstress* at the Royal Academy the following year. Compositionally similar to the previous picture, this work was inspired by the lines from Thomas Hood's *Song of the Shirt* which were included with the catalogue entry:

> Oh! men with sisters dear,
>   Oh! men with mothers and wives,
> It is not linen you're wearing out,
>   But human creatures' lives.

The critical response was again favorable. The reviewer for *The Illustrated London News* called it "a very good picture, both as to conception and execution" (May 11, 1844, pp. 305-306). His counterpart at the *Art Union* wrote,

> The story is told in such a way as to approach the best feelings of the human heart: she is not a low-born drudge to proclaim her patient endurance to the vulgar world; her suffering is read only in the shrunken cheek, and the eye feverish and dim with watching. The work bears every evidence of attentive study and is a worthy illustration of Mr. Hood's verses (1844, p. 158).

Thackeray was, however, unimpressed. As Michael Angelo Titmarsh he complained in *Fraser's Magazine*,

> Frater Redgrave. . . . In the namby pamby line his errors are very sad. Has he not been already warned in this very miscellany of his propensity to small sentiment? Has he corrected himself of that grievous tendancy? No (The Oxford Thackeray, Vol. II, p. 614).

Despite Thackeray's dismissal of his "small sentiment," the concern with the plight of women manifested in Redgrave's pictures from the 1840s was a response to the very limited opportunities open to women in Victorian England. For the woman who had to support herself almost the only alternative to domestic service or the dreary existence depicted here was prostitution, and Redgrave's downtrodden subjects anticipate the fallen women painted by the Pre-Raphaelites in the 1850s. Hood's *Song of the Shirt*, which was published in 1843, also inspired one of a group of four gloomily realist pictures painted around 1850 by George Frederic Watts (q.v.). However, social comment only became widespread in the work of a younger generation of Victorian painters, including Frank Holl (q.v.), Luke Fildes (q.v.), and Hubert

von Herkomer (q.v.), who came into prominence in the 1870s. Holl, in fact, painted a picture based upon the *Song of the Shirt* (Thomas Agnew & Sons, London) over two decades after Redgrave exhibited *The Sempstress*.

In his autobiography Redgrave offered the following observations on his pictures of social comment:

> I had in view the 'helping them to right that suffer wrong' at the hands of their fellow countrymen. If this has been done feebly, it has at least been done from the heart, and I trust . . . I shall never have occasion to regret that I have debased the art I love by making it subservient to an unworthy end.

Provenance

P. Horthewick

Anon. Sale: Sotheby's Belgravia, London, March 27, 1973, Lot 49, reproduced.

Fine Art Society, London (Agents).

58. * THE CHILDREN IN THE WOOD—THE MORNING

Oil on canvas: 14-1/4 x 12-1/4 inches
Inscribed, lower right: *Rich^d, Redgrave 1859*

The Children in the Wood — The Morning is one of Redgrave's earliest pictures painted in an almost completely Pre-Raphaelite manner. As the reviewer for the *Art Journal* put it:

> The emulation in painting of what are called "bits of nature" seems to grow year by year. This is not so much the story of the Babes in the Wood, as a study from the wood itself.

Millais's *Ophelia*, exhibited in 1852 (Tate Gallery), is probably the best-known example of this Pre-Raphaelite preoccupation with nature. It

(continued on page 151)

R. Redgrave, *The Lost Path*
(Photograph: Sotheby's Belgravia)

57. R. Redgrave, *The Sempstress.*

58. R. Redgrave, *The Children in the Wood — The Morning.*

BRITON RIVIERE, RA
(1840-1920)

came from an artistic family of Huguenots living in London. His grandfather Daniel Valentine Riviere (who exhibited at the Royal Academy from 1823 to 1840), his father William Riviere (1806-1876), an uncle Henry Parsons Riviere (1811-1888), an aunt Miss F. Riviere (exhibited 1831 to 1834), and a sister, Annette L. Riviere (exhibited 1870 to 1887), were all painters, although none attained the degree of success achieved by Briton Riviere.

Born on August 14, 1840, Riviere received his primary education at Cheltenham College, where his father was Master of the drawing school. When he was eleven, two of his pictures, *Love at First Sight* and *Kitten and Tom Tit* were exhibited at the British Institution. Eventually, Riviere entered Oxford (his father left Cheltenham to become Teacher of Painting at Oxford in 1859), where he received a B.A. in 1867 and an M.A. in 1873. Prior to entering Oxford, Riviere made his debut at the Royal Academy in 1858 with three pictures. Nine years later, before his marriage to the painter Mary Alice Dobell (exhibited 1869 to 1870), he attained his first great public success with a picture entitled *The Long Sleep* which showed a just deceased shepherd forlornly looked upon by his dog. Riviere painted historical and literary works, usually involving animals, but his most popular pictures were sympathetic depictions of man and his "best friend" in works with titles such as *Prisoners, The Last of the Garrison, Charity, Sympathy* and *Come back!* Describing Riviere's work in 1884, F. G. Stephens declared that he

> had with true sympathy hit on a treasury of fancy the public could never turn from. . . .
> He is one of the few painters who have hit the happy mean between the utter savagery and brute force of Rubens's and Snyder's beasts and those somewhat genteel animals Sir Edwin Landseer [q.v.] painted after he 'got into society.'

Not only the public but also his fellow artists approved of Riviere's work. In 1878, he was elected an Associate Academician, in 1881, a full Academician and in 1896, after the death of John Everett Millais (q.v.), he just missed being elected President of the Royal Academy. He led the first two ballots, but on the third, four of the five Academicians who had supported Frank Dicksee (q.v.) switched their votes to Edward Poynter (q.v.), making the final count Riviere: 16, Poynter: 19. Riviere died in London on April 20, 1920. During his long career, he exhibited one hundred and forty-two works at the Academy.

Bibliography

W. W. Fenn, "Briton Riviere, RA" in *Some Modern Artists and Their Work*, ed. Wilfred Meynell, London, 1883, pp. 141-147.

Frederick G. Stephens, *Artists at Home*, New York, 1884.

59. ON THE ROAD TO GLOUCESTER FAIR

Oil on canvas: 23 x 84 inches
Original frame

This early work is not typical of the bulk of Riviere's *oeuvre*. He had not yet developed the sympathetic interplay between man and dog that was to bring him fame and fortune. The only aspect of the picture which might possibly be said to foreshadow this is the playful interaction between the dog and the cow in the center of the picture.

On the Road to Gloucester Fair received no notice in the major reviews of the Royal Academy exhibition of 1859, where it was exhibited for the first time. Stylistically, the picture is somewhat reminiscent of the collaborative work of Frederick Richard Lee (q.v.) and Thomas Sidney Cooper (q.v.), although it lacks the luminous detail and romantic feeling of Lee's landscapes. The pastoral subject matter of the picture carries on the tradition of painters like George Morland (1763-1804) and James Ward (1769-1859).

Provenance

Anon. Sale: Christie's, London, December 15, 1972, Lot 44.

Fine Art Society, London (Agents).

Exhibitions

Royal Academy, 1859, No. 563.

References

W. W. Fenn, "Briton Riviere, RA," in *Some Modern Artists and Their Work*, ed. Wilfrid Meynell, London, 1883, p. 144.

Frederick G. Stephens, *Artists at Home*, New York, 1884, p. 70.

59. B. Riviere, *On the Road to Gloucester Fair.*

DAVID ROBERTS, RA
(1796-1864)

was born in Stockbridge, near Edinburgh, on October 24, 1796, the son of a shoemaker. He manifested a talent for drawing at a very young age, but when his drawings were shown to the Master of the Trustees Academy in Edinburgh, Roberts was told that, in light of his family's circumstances, he should be apprenticed to a house painter in order to be able to earn a living. Shortly thereafter, he began working for an ornamental interior painter named Gavin Beugo. Upon the termination of his seven-year apprenticeship, he became at the age of twenty-one the scene painter for Bannister's circus. The bankruptcy of this enterprise forced him to take up house painting again for a brief period until he was able to get the job of assistant scene painter at the Parthenon Theater in Edinburgh. A backdrop depicting a Roman street was a great success, and Roberts was hired by the Theatre Royal. The higher salary of thirty shillings per week made him feel prosperous enough to get married, and while working there, he became acquainted with and began a long friendship with his future fellow landscape painter, Clarkson Stanfield (1795-1867). In 1822, at Stanfield's suggestion, Roberts submitted three pictures to an exhibition in Edinburgh, and much to his surprise, two of them sold for fifty shillings. This success prompted him to go to London, where he was eventually engaged along with Stanfield as a scene painter at the Drury Lane Theatre. In 1826, his *View of Rouen Cathedral* was exhibited at the Royal Academy and he began working at the Covent Garden Theatre. The following year he designed and painted the sets for the first London production of Mozart's *Il Seraglio*. In 1830 he made his first extended trip abroad and two years later, on the advice of David Wilkie (q.v.), he toured France, Spain, and Morocco. Paintings and a book, *Picturesque Sketches in Spain during the years 1832 and 1833*, derived from hundreds of sketches made on this trip, occupied Roberts for the next four years. In 1838 he was elected an Associate Academician, and he embarked upon a long sojourn in Egypt and the Holy Land. The six-volume *Views in the Holy Land, Syria, Idumea, Arabia, Egypt, and Nubia*, published from 1842 to 1849, as well as numerous watercolors and oil paintings, resulted from this trip. In 1841 Roberts was elevated to the rank of full Academician.

In his early works, Roberts employed bright colors, but after his trip to the Middle East, his palette became colder and more somber. The architectural accuracy of Roberts's work established him with Stanfield as one of the leading topographical landscape painters of his day. John Ruskin (1819-1900) was an early admirer

of his work, but by the 1850s, he began to criticize Roberts's artificiality. Throughout his lifetime Roberts continued to travel frequently. The proceeds from his books and his large output of paintings and drawings (he exhibited one hundred and one works at the Royal Academy alone) made Roberts a wealthy man. He died on November 25, 1864, while working on a series of pictures entitled *London from the River Thames*.

Bibliography

"British Artists: Their Style and Character: No. XXXVI — David Roberts, RA," *Art Journal*, 1858, pp. 201-203.
James Ballantine, *The Life of David Roberts*, RA, Edinburgh, 1866.
Allan Cunningham, *Lives of the Most Eminent British Painters*, London, 1879-1880, Vol. III, pp. 363-376 (revised edition, annotated and continued to the present time by Mrs. Charles Heaton).
James L. Caw, *Scottish Painting, Past and Present 1620-1908*, Edinburgh, 1908, pp. 153-155.

60. * VIEW SHOWING THE ENTRANCE TO THE FIRTH OF FORTH, WITH A PROPOSED RECONSTRUCTION OF THE TEMPLE OF THE SYBIL, AT TIVOLI, ON THE ROCK OF DRUMSAPIE, NEAR QUEEN'S DRIVE, IN QUEEN'S PARK, EDINBURGH

Oil on canvas, in an arched mount: 19 x 48 inches
Inscribed, lower right: *David Roberts R.A. 1852*
Original frame

The Firth of Forth was the only landscape of his native Scotland among the one hundred and one pictures which David Roberts exhibited at the Royal Academy. Even this panorama of a location no more than a few miles from the place of his birth has had a Roman temple superimposed upon it. Nor for those unfamiliar with the actual site, except for the title itself, is there much either in the atmosphere or the quality of the landscape to suggest that the setting is Scotland. This did not seem to upset contemporary critics. The reviewer for *The Illustrated London News* wrote, "the Hanging Committee has deservedly assigned places of honour to ... Roberts's small picture of *The Firth of Forth*," while his

counterpart at the *Art Journal* enthused, "no more enchanting passage of landscape is to be found in the Morea, Livadia, or even in the Greek islands." The latter did complain, however, that "the temple should not have been placed so near the centre of the composition."

Provenance
Stretford Corporation, formerly part of the Longford Hall Collection (Sale: Christie's, London, July 2, 1971, Lot 74).
Fine Art Society, London (Agents).

Exhibitions
Royal Academy, 1854, No. 581.

References
Art Journal, 1854, p. 165.
"Our Critic Among the Painters," *Punch*, 1854, p. 247-248.
The Illustrated London News Supplement, May 6, 1854, p. 426.
James Ballantine, *The Life of David Roberts*, RA, Edinburgh, 1866, pp. 176, 251.

60. D. Roberts, *View Showing the Entrance to the
Firth of Forth, with a Proposed Reconstruction
of the Temple of the Sibyl, at
Tivoli, on the Rock of Drumsapie,
near Queen's Drive, in Queen's Park, Edinburgh.*
(*see color Plate XXIII, p. 181*)

MATTHIAS ROBINSON

(d. 1884)

first exhibited at the Royal Academy in 1856. His entry was a modest work, entitled *Blossoms in May,* which showed two girls grouped in sisterly fashion under a branch of May blossoms. Besides commenting that the prominence of this branch injured the effect of the picture, the reviewer of the *Art Journal* also observed that the painting was "singularly like the work of Maclise." Ending on a more optimistic note, he concluded that "the drawing is unexceptionable, and although there is a degree of hardness in the outline, the work is one of good promise." Apparently this promise remained unfulfilled as Robinson had only two more works accepted at the Academy during the rest of his career. He did, however, exhibit more frequently at the Society of British Artists and at the British Institution. Some time between 1856 and 1863, the last year he was represented at the Royal Academy, he abandoned his "Maclise" style and began painting humorous genre scenes involving children, after the manner popularized by Thomas Webster (q.v.). Robinson died in 1884.

Bibliography

Christopher Wood, *The Dictionary of Victorian Painters,* London, 1971, p. 139.

what direct contact, if any, he had with the members of the Cranbrook Colony. Their influence on his work is, nonetheless, very apparent in *The Battle of the Bolsters.*

Provenance

Anon. Sale: Christie's, London, July 11, 1969, Lot 82.
Fine Art Society, London.

Exhibitions

Royal Academy, 1863, No. 667.
The Art and Mind of Victorian England: Paintings from the Forbes Magazine Collection, University Gallery, University of Minnesota, Minneapolis, 1974, No. 41 (reproduced in catalogue).

References

Art Journal, 1863, p. 112.
Christopher Wood, *The Dictionary of Victorian Painters,* London, 1971, reproduced p. 361.
Melvin Waldfogel, "Introduction," *The Art and Mind of Victorian England: Paintings from the Forbes Magazine Collection,* University Gallery, University of Minnesota, Minneapolis, 1974, p. 21 (exhibition catalogue).

61. THE BATTLE OF THE BOLSTERS

Oil on canvas: 12-1/4 x 18-1/4 inches
Inscribed, lower right: *MR*

The Battle of the Bolsters was classified in the *Art Journal* as a "good example [of] the School which follows after David Wilkie . . . derived primarily from the Dutch . . . small in size, generally simple and often even trivial in incident . . . and for execution it may almost be said, the more detail the better." The reviewer went on to say Thomas Webster (q.v.) "has in this line long taken the lead." Robinson has followed Webster's lead in this picture, but his work lacks his model's technical competence. He was not alone in working in the manner of Webster. A group of artists, including Frederick Daniel Hardy (1826-1911), George Bernard O'Neill (1828-1917), Augustus E. Mulready (d. 1886) and George Hardy (1822-1909), settled around Webster at Cranbrook in Kent, and painted, with varying degrees of success, small unpretentious genre scenes, usually involving children, similar to Webster's (see Appendix I). Robinson resided in Chelsea, and it is not known

61. M. Robinson, *The Battle of the Bolsters*.

JAMES SMETHAM
(1821-1889)

was born in Pateley Bridge, Yorkshire on September 9, 1821, the son of a Methodist minister. He was educated at a Methodist institution and then apprenticed to an architect in Lincoln, E. J. Wilson. While working in the latter's offices, he became acquainted with the landscape painter Peter de Wint (1784-1849), who encouraged him to become an artist. In the 1840s Smetham studied in London at Cary's Academy and at the Royal Academy Schools. He supported himself by teaching drawing at the Wesleyan Normal College and with occasional portrait commissions. In 1851, he made his debut at the Royal Academy Summer Exhibitions with three works, two of which were portaits. About this time Smetham came under the influence of John Ruskin (1819-1900), two years his senior, and in 1854, he was one of the first three pupils to enroll under Ruskin's instruction when the Working Men's College opened that fall. During the 1850s, he painted in a detailed naturalisitc style, heavily influenced by the Pre-Raphaelites (see Appendix I) whose cause Ruskin had espoused. Smetham developed a close friendship with Dante Gabriel Rossetti (1828-1882), and from 1863 to 1868 he is said to have spent every Wednesday at the latter's studio. However, by this time Smetham had already abandoned the Pre-Raphaelite style in favor of more broadly painted pictures which were symbolic rather than factual records of nature.

The esteem which Smetham had held for Ruskin eventually was transferred to the landscape painters, John Linnell (q.v.) and Samuel Palmer (1805-1881), both of whose pictures Smetham's later works somewhat resemble. These two artists formed a link to William Blake (1757-1827), who Smetham also greatly admired, and about whose biography by Alexander Gilchrist he wrote a long review first published in the *Quarterly Review* in 1868 and reprinted in the second edition of the book itself.

Smetham had suffered a mental breakdown in 1857 and twenty years later experienced a complete collapse which left him insane for the last twelve years of his life. Smetham ceased to exhibit at the Royal Academy eight years before going completely mad and after having shown only eighteen pictures there. He died on February 6, 1889.

Bibliography
S. Smetham and W. Davies, *The Letters of James Smetham*, London, 1891.
"James Smetham and C. Allson Collins," *Art Journal*, 1904, pp. 281-284.
William Beardmore, *James Smetham, Poet and Essayist*, London, 1906.
Geoffrey Grigson, "James Smetham," *Cornhill Magazine*, No. 976, Autumn 1948, pp. 332-346.

62. *CHRIST AT EMMAUS
Oil on panel: 19-3/4 x 15-3/4 inches

Christ at Emmaus was the first of two biblical subjects exhibited by Smetham at the Royal Academy, the second being *The Hymn of the Lord's Supper* exhibited in 1869. The earlier picture is based on the story told in the Gospel of St. Luke, Ch. 24: 13-36 of the miraculous appearance of Christ to two of His Disciples following the Resurrection:

13 And, Behold, two of them went that same day to a village called Emmaus, which was from Jerusalem *about* three score furlongs.

• • • •

15 And it came to pass, that, while they communed *together* and reasoned, Jesus himself drew near, and went with them.

• • • •

30 And it came to pass, as he sat at meat with them, he took bread, and blessed *it,* and broke and gave to them.

• • • •

31 And their eyes were opened, and they knew him; and he vanished out of their sight.

This subject is one of the most frequently painted in the history of art. Although in Protestant England religious subjects were relatively rare, David Wilkie (q.v.) had begun a sketch of *The Supper at Emmaus* on his trip to the East in 1840-41. Smetham may have seen it in the memorial exhibition of Wilkie's work at the British Institution in 1842.

At the time he painted *Christ at Emmaus,* Smetham had been reading the writings of John Ruskin (1819-1900), and he was determined to paint in what he called "a severely imitational style." The picture predates Smetham's personal association with Rossetti (1828-1882) and other members of the Pre-Raphaelite group, and it is questionable if he had fallen under Pre-Raphaelite influence as early as 1852. But the sense of spiritual intensity in the Disciples' response to Christ's revelation, as well as the picture's precise detail, suggests why in the following years Ruskin and Rossetti were ready to take a keen interest in Smetham's art. His almost naively direct visualization of a miraculous experience makes understandable Rossetti's comment, published in Gilchrist's *Life of Blake* in 1863, that Smetham was closely akin to Blake, "more so probably than any other living artist could be said to be."

Provenance
Mr. Winders, bought in 1856.
Anon. Sale: Christie's, London, December 10, 1963, Lot 196.
Charles and Lavinia Handley-Read, London.
Fine Art Society, London (Agents for the seller).

Exhibitions
Royal Academy, 1852, No. 23.
Victorian and Edwardian Decorative Art: The Handley-Read Collection, Fine Art Society, London, 1974, No. 74 (reproduced in catalogue).

References
S. Smetham and W. Davies, *The Letters of James Smetham,* London, 1891, p. 16.

62. J. Smetham, *Christ at Emmaus*.

GEORGE ADOLPHUS STOREY, RA

(1834-1919)

was born in London on the 7th of January, 1834. As a child he was much interested in painting although it was not until 1850 that he decided to take it up as a career. Two years earlier he had been sent to Paris to study mathematics and upon his return, he tried working in an architect's office. Finding architecture too dry, he entered J. M. Leigh's art school in Newman Street and two years later made his debut at the Royal Academy with *A Family Portrait*. While at Leigh's he became acquainted with Charles Robert Leslie (q.v.), from whom he received advice and training. He entered the Royal Academy Schools in 1854, and in 1862 he visited Spain remaining several months in Madrid.

Storey's pictures are principally portraits, quasi-historical and literary subjects. A resident of St. John's Wood, he was a member of the St. John's Wood Clique (see Appendix I). His first work to attract special notice was *The Meeting of William Seymour and the Lady Arabella Stuart, at the Court of James I, 1609*, exhibited at the Royal Academy in 1864. In 1876, Storey benefited from an expansion of the number of Associates permitted by the Academy and along with a number of others including Sir Lawrence Alma-Tadema (q.v.), Eyre Crowe (q.v.) Edwin Long (1829-1891) and John Wright Oakes (1820-1887) was elected to that rank. In 1900, he was appointed Teacher of Perspective. It was not until 1914 that he was finally made a full Academician. This promotion entitled him to the rank of Professor of Perspective. Storey published an autobiography in 1899 and died twenty years later on the 29th of July, 1919, having exhibited a total of one hundred and seventy-two works at the Royal Academy during his long career.

Bibliography

Art Journal, 1875, pp. 173-176.
Frederic G. Stephens, *Artists at Home*, New York, 1884.
G. A. Storey, *Sketches from Memory*, London, 1899.
Connoisseur, September 1919, pp. 52-53 (obituary)
Bevis Hillier, "The St. John's Wood Clique," *Apollo*, June, 1964, pp. 490-495.

63. * ORPHANS

Oil on canvas: 41 x 59 inches
Inscribed, lower left: *G. A. Storey . 1879*
Original frame

This picture, although contemporary with some of the greatest late Victorian social realist pictures dealing with bereavement, lacks the dramatic impact of *The Lord Gave, and the Lord Hath Taken Away* exhibited in 1869 by Frank Holl (q.v.), or *The Widower* exhibited in 1876 by Luke Fildes (q.v.). It is rather a charming and sentimental genre scene of the type so profitably turned out by John Everett Millais (q.v.) in his later years, and by several of the members of the St. John's Wood Clique (see Appendix I). It shows two recently orphaned children still in their mourning clothes being delivered to an orphanage; visible through the door is the carriage that brought them and a manservant carrying in their trunk. The sorrow of the subject is mitigated by the knowledge that the new arrivals will soon have as playmates the bright-eyed little girls at the table on the left, who seem far from unhappy with their lot.

When *Orphans* appeared at the Royal Academy exhibition of 1879, the critical reception was generally favorable, if luke warm. The *Art Journal* described it as "very touching and tender" while *The Illustrated London News* concluded with little enthusiasm, "a mildly pathetic picture." From *Punch* came the sarcastic query, "Orphans! And who made them so? Oh, you Storey!"

Like many of Storey's works, *Orphans* gives evidence of the strong influence of paintings of interior scenes by Pieter de Hooch and other seventeenth-century Dutch artists. The lack of shadow in the landscape seen out the door, the sharp outlines, and the areas of unmodulated color creating a strong sense of pattern are qualities that appear in the work of several of the St. John's Wood artists, most notably H. Stacy Marks (1829-1898). Their tendency toward a high-keyed decorative flatness was paralleled in the contemporary book illustrations of Randolph Caldecott (1846-1886) and Walter Crane (1845-1915), which a decade later were to have an influence upon Paul Gauguin (1848-1903) and his circle in France.

Provenance

Anon. Sale: Sotheby's Belgravia, London, November 20, 1973, Lot 58a, reproduced.
Fine Art Society, London (Agents).

Exhibitions

Royal Academy, 1879, No. 80.

References

Art Journal, 1879, p. 127.
Henry Blackburn, *Academy Notes*, London, 1879, p. 14, reproduced p. 14.
The Illustrated London News, May 17, 1879, p. 471.
"The Tour of the Royal Academy," *Punch*, May 24, 1879, p. 229.
Frederick G. Stephens, *Artists at Home*, New York, 1884, p. 90.

63. G. A. Storey, *Orphans*.

JAMES JACQUES JOSEPH TISSOT

(1836-1902)

was born in Nantes on October 15, 1836. His father was a man of means and an avid conchologist. Tissot was educated at the local Jesuit College and then in 1856 was allowed to go to Paris to study at the *Ecole des Beaux Arts*. There he met Whistler (1834-1903) and later Degas (1834-1912). He studied under the fashionable Second Empire painter Hippolyte Flandrin (1809-1864), but it was the Belgian Master, Baron Hendrik Leys (1815-1869), whom he visited in Antwerp in the late 1850s, who exerted the strongest influence on his work. He made his *Salon* debut in 1859, and in 1861 the Government purchased his *Faust et Marguerite*. Three years later he had an untitled medieval subject accepted at the Royal Academy. It was the first of the seventeen works which he eventually exhibited there. Shortly thereafter he painted his first pictures of modern life. In 1869 he visited England, and began contributing cartoons to *Vanity Fair,* which he continued to do until 1877. After the collapse of the Second Empire and the occupation of Paris by the Prussians in 1871, he played a minor role in the Commune. He found it discreet to adjourn to London when the Commune itself collapsed. In 1872 he began exhibiting at the Royal Academy again and in 1874 he refused Degas's invitation to participate in the first Impressionist Exhibition. His first social conversation piece, *Too Early,* exhibited at the Academy in 1873, was a great success and Tissot followed with other similar works. He showed ten such pictures at the inaugural exhibition of Sir Coutts Lindsay's Grosvenor Gallery where Ruskin (1819-1900) described them as "mere coloured photographs of vulgar society" (*Works,* Vol. XXIX, p. 160). Around 1867, Kathleen Newton, a divorcée, became his mistress. Her death from tuberculosis in November of 1882 caused Tissot to return to Paris. Three years later he exhibited his *Quinze Tableaux sur la Femme à Paris;* in 1889 his *Return of the Prodigal Son in Modern Life,* which had first been shown at the Dudley Gallery in 1882, won a Gold Medal at the *Universal Exhibition*. He visited the Holy Land three times and in 1894 unveiled some 270 drawings illustrating *The Life of Christ* (Brooklyn Museum). He died at Buillon, near Besançon, in his family's chateau on August 8, 1902 while at work on a series of Old Testament illustrations, which are now in the Jewish Museum, New York.

Bibliography

James Laver, *Vulgar Society: The Romantic Career of James Tissot 1836-1902,* London, 1936.
Henri Zerner, David S. Brooke and Michael Wentworth, *James Jacques Joseph Tissot,* Museum of Art, Rhode Island School of Design, Providence, and The Art Gallery of Ontario, Toronto, 1968 (exhibition catalogue).

64. * 'GOOD BYE' — ON THE MERSEY

Oil on canvas: 33 x 21 inches
Inscribed, lower right: *J J Tissot*

'Good Bye' — On the Mersey was Tissot's last Royal Academy exhibit, and it was a particularly appropriate one. A year later, after the tragic death of his mistress, he left England never to return. The scene is in the harbor of Liverpool, whose buildings are visible in the background. The figures in the foreground are apparently on a ferry crossing the River Mersey from Birkenhead on the opposite side. Liverpool was the chief port in England for ships going to the United States and Canada, so the large ship in the middle distance is, in all probability, starting out on a transatlantic crossing.

The subject makes the picture an interesting work to compare with Ford Madox Brown's (1821-1893) *Last of England* of 1855 (Birmingham City Art Gallery). Besides the contrast of Brown's bright Pre-Raphaelite palette to Tissot's considerably more subdued one, the most notable difference in the two works is that in Brown's the protagonists dramatically confront the viewer while in the Tissot their backs are turned. While Brown's picture has a message about emigration and its consequences for his characters, who have been forced to leave their native land by financial necessity, Tissot's picture is more ambiguous. The figures in his foreground are of a more prosperous class than those in Brown's work, and they are not the ones who are leaving. They watch the spectacle of the departure of an ocean liner and participate in the ritual of waving good-bye to voyagers whom they probably do not even know. In 1879 Tissot had exhibited a picture entitled *Emigrants* at the Grosvenor Gallery. An oil sketch in the Museum of Art, Rhode Island School of Design, and a related etching, which is entitled *Les Deux Amis* and dated 1881 in the plate, show a more intimate dockside scene of the departure of a ship bound for America.

Tissot executed many additional shipboard subjects but this is the most subdued and introverted of all of them. The woman standing closest to us is Kathleen Newton, who appears in many of the pictures painted by Tissot between 1876 and 1882.

Provenance

Anon. Sale: Christie's, London, July 10, 1970, Lot 151, reproduced.

Exhibitions

Royal Academy, 1881, No. 981.
The Second James Tissot Exhibition, Leicester Galleries, 1937, No. 118.
On loan to The Metropolitan Museum of Art, New York, January, 1974 - March, 1975, No. L. 1973. 1. 3

References

Art Journal, 1881, p. 230.
Henry Blackburn, *Academy Notes,* London, 1881, p. 230.
The Illustrated London News, May 21, 1881, p. 498.
James Laver, *Vulgar Society: The Romantic Career of James Tissot 1836-1902,* London, 1936, pp. 48, 68.
Henri Zerner, David S. Brooke and Michael Wentworth, *James Jacques Joseph Tissot,* Museum of Art, Rhode Island School of Design, Providence, and the Art Gallery of Ontario, Toronto, 1968, No. 33 (exhibition catalogue).
"Mr. Forbes Adds a Tearjerker," *Evening News,* London, July 10, 1970.
Terence Mullaly, "Ladbrooke Landscape Fetches 3,600 gns.," *The Daily Telegraph,* London, July 11, 1970.

F. M. Brown, *The Last of England*
(Museum and Art Gallery, Birmingham)

64. J. Tissot, 'Good-bye' — On the Mersey.

EDWARD MATTHEW WARD, RA

(1816-1879)

was born in Pimlico, then a suburb of London, on July 14, 1816. As a child he manifested an exceptional interest in art which was encouraged by his parents. His father showed some of his early pictures to the sculptor Sir Francis Chantrey (1781-1841) who recommended that Ward should submit himself to the rigors of formal, academic training. Through the good offices of David Wilkie (q.v.), he was enrolled as a pupil in the Royal Academy Schools in 1834. That year he made his first appearance at the Academy's exhibition with a portrait of *Mr. O. Smith, Comedian, in the Character of Don Quixote.* In 1835, a small scene from Sterne's *Sentimental Journey* which he submitted to the Academy was accepted, but not hung due to a lack of space. The following year, Ward went to Rome where he entered the Academy of St. Luke, and in 1838 he won that Institution's Silver Medal for historical composition. His *Cimabue and Giotto,* painted while Ward was still in Rome, was exhibited at the Royal Academy in 1839 where it was very favorably reviewed, thus establishing his reputation as an up-and-coming artist.

While en route back to England, Ward stopped in Munich where he studied fresco under Peter Cornelius (1783-1867) for a few months. Shortly after his return home, Ward was drawn into The Clique (see Appendix I). In 1846, he was elected an Associate Academician and in 1855, a full Academician. Two years after becoming an ARA, Ward married Henrietta Ward (1832-1924), the daughter of the miniaturist George Raphael Ward (1797-1879), granddaughter of the animal painter James Ward (1769-1859), and a painter in her own right, who began exhibiting at the Royal Academy the year after their marriage.

Ward entered the competitions for the decoration of the Houses of Parliament (see Appendix II), and in 1855 he was given a commission for eight scenes to decorate the corridor leading to the House of Commons. In 1858, he was commissioned by Queen Victoria to commemorate *The Royal Visit to the Tomb of Napoleon I* and *The Investment of the Garter upon Napoleon III.* From 1834 to 1877, when he last showed at the Academy, Ward exhibited eighty-six pictures there, principally of historical or literary subjects. In the early 1860s, he was afflicted by mental disorders, and he died during a particularly acute crisis in Windsor on January 15, 1879.

Bibliography

"Portraits of British Artists; No. 6—Edward Matthew Ward, ARA," *Art Union,* 1847, p. 260.
"British Artists: Their Style and Character; No. II—Edward Matthew Ward, ARA," *Art Journal,* 1855, pp. 45-48.
Art Journal, 1879, pp. 72-73 (obituary).
James Dafforne, *The Life and Works of Edward Matthew Ward,* London, 1879.

65. A YEAR AFTER THE BATTLE: THE MOMENTO SCENE AT DINAN BRITTANY

Oil on canvas: 36-1/4 x 28-1/4 inches
Inscribed, lower right: *E M Ward RA 1876*
Original slip frame

This picture was exhibited by Ward in 1876, the next to the last year in which he exhibited at the Royal Academy before insanity brought his painting career to a halt. Three of his five pictures shown in 1876 were identified in the catalogue as subjects from Brittany and Normandy, two of them being of Dinan. These pictures representing scenes from contemporary life in France, rather than episodes drawn from literature or history, were a complete departure from Ward's previous practice.

The Franco-Prussian War (1870-71) provided painters on both sides of the Channel with much inspiring subject matter. In France several artists, Edouard Detaille (1848-1912) and Alphonse de Neuville (1835-1885) most prominent among them, won on canvas the laurels the army failed to win on the field. Ward, however, did not look to "La Gloire" in his souvenir of the war. Instead he reduced the heroic corpses sprawled dramatically across the canvases of his continental counterparts to the human scale of the grief of the widow of but one slain soldier. Sentiment rather than valor is Ward's message following the pattern of the response of several Victorian painters to the Crimean War, as seen for example in *Peace Concluded, 1856* (Minneapolis Institute of Arts) by Millais (q.v.). The old veteran on the left recalls the most famous English picture of the domestic aftermath of a battle, *Chelsea Pensioners Receiving the London Gazette Extraordinary of Thursday, June 22nd 1815, Announcing the Battle of Waterloo!!!,* exhibited by David Wilkie (q.v) in 1822 (Apsley House, London). More recently, veterans in a church were the subject of *The Last Muster—Sunday at the Royal Hospital, Chelsea* (Lady Lever Art Gallery, Port Sunlight), exhibited by Hubert von Herkomer (q.v.) in 1875, the year before Ward's picture. For his efforts, Ward had his *The Year After the Battle* categorized among "sundry bits of genre" by the critic of the *Art Journal* in his review of the Academy exhibition of 1876.

Provenance

New South Wales Art Gallery
Anon. Sale: Sotheby's Belgravia, London, October 24, 1972, reproduced.

Exhibitions

Royal Academy, 1876, No. 239.

References

Art Journal, 1876, p. 216.
Henry Blackburn, *Academy Notes,* London, 1876, p. 29, reproduced p. 29.
The Illustrated London News, May 6, 1876, p. 450.

A. de Neuville, *The Line of Retreat*
(*Forbes* Magazine Collection, New York)

65. E. M. Ward, *A Year after the Battle: The Momento Scene at Dinan Brittany.*

JOHN WILLIAM WATERHOUSE, RA
(1849-1917)

was born in Rome in 1849. His father was a painter from Leeds who specialized in copying Old Masters, and this was why he was in Rome when his son was born. Young Waterhouse began his training with his father, and he furthered it by copying pictures in the National Gallery and South Kensington Museum. In 1871 he entered the Royal Academy Schools. The work of Lawrence Alma-Tadema (q.v.) and his follower Edwin Long (1829-1891) exerted a strong influence on him, but eventually he also adopted some of the languorous ethereal qualities of the late work of Edward Burne-Jones (1833-1898). He worked on a large scale and painted biblical, historical and literary subjects. In 1874, he made his debut at the Academy with *Sleep and His Half Brother Death*. He was elected an Associate of the Royal Academy in 1885, and an Academician ten years later. He also became a Member of the Royal Institute of Painters in Watercolours. In 1889 he won a Silver Medal at the *Exposition Universelle* in Paris. Before his death in 1917 he showed eighty-four works at the Royal Academy.

Bibliography

Alfred L. Baldry, "J. W. Waterhouse and His Works," *Studio*, Vol. IV, January, 1895, pp. 102-115.
"Some Drawings by J. W. Waterhouse, RA," *Studio*, Vol. XLIV, September, 1908, pp. 247-252.
"John William Waterhouse, RA: His Life and Work," *Art Annual: Supplement to the Art Journal*, 1909.
Studio, VOL. LXX, 1917, p. 88 (obituary).

66. * MARIAMNE

Oil on canvas: 102 x 71 inches
Inscribed, lower right: *J. W. Waterhouse 1887*
Original frame

was first exhibited at the Royal Academy in 1887. The catalogue included a full description of the incident portrayed:

> Mariamne, wife of King Herod the Great, going forth to execution after her trial for the false charges brought against her by the jealousy of Salome, the king's sister, his mother, and others of his family. After Mariamne's trial and condemnation by the judges appointed by her husband, Herod, who had been passionately attached to his wife, was about to commute the sentence of death carried out, which was accordingly done.

The source of this passage is *The Jewish Antiquities* by Flavius Josephus (c. 37-95 A.D.). *Herod and Mariamne* was the subject of a tragedy by the German dramatist Friedrich Hebbel which was first performed in 1849. It is possible that Waterhouse's interest in the subject was inspired by Hebbel's treatment, although his visualization does not correspond to any scene in the play. The actual execution of Mariamne took place in 29 B.C.. King Herold the Great and his sister are not the same Herod (who was the son of this Herod) and Salome who were reponsible for the death of John the Baptist, but the stories of a Salome who in each case manipulated the ruler to bring about the death of an innocent person are comparable (before Richard Strauss wrote his opera *Salome*, Kaiser Wilhelm had proposed the subject of *Herod and Mariamne*). In the many later nineteenth-century pictures of *Salome*, such as the painting exhibited by Gustave Moreau (1826-1898) in the *Salon* of 1876, the focus is upon the *femme fatale;* in Waterhouses's *Mariamne*, although the theme of the power of woman over man is certainly present, the heroine is a victim on her way to martyrdom.

The reviewer for the *Magazine of Art*, while conceding that the picture was "noble and impressive" was disappointed that it showed "no significant departure in style or aim." This did not stop the *Magazine of Art* from using the picture as its frontispiece the following year. The critic in the *Art Journal* declared it, "emphatically one of the pictures of the year," but complained that "probably the accessories are too pronounced."

Waterhouse was awarded a Silver Medal for *Mariamne* when it was shown in Paris at the *Exposition Universelle* of 1889.

Provenance

Sir Cuthbert Quilter, Bart. (Sale: Christie's, London, July 9, 1909, Lot 86, 480 gns.).
H. Smith
Leopold Alber (Sale: Christie's, London, July 15, 1938, Lot 49, 48 gns.).
Mrs. E. M. Stirling, Old Battersea House, London
The Trustees of the De Morgan Foundation (Sale: Christie's, London, November 20, 1970, Lot 286).
Thomas Agnew & Sons, London (Agents).

Exhibitions

Royal Academy, 1887, No. 134.
The City Art Gallery, Manchester, 1887.
Exposition Universelle, Paris, 1889, No. 155, Silver Medal.
Spring Exhibition, St. Jude's, Whitechapel, 1890, No. 9.
World's Columbian Exhibition, Chicago, 1893, No. 482.
Guild Hall, 1894, No. 20.
Exposition Internationale, Brussels, 1897, No. 146.
West Ham, 1897.
Camberwell, 1899 and 1903.
Bemondsey Settlement, 1900.
Southward, 1900.
Nottingham, 1903.
Whitestable, 1904.
Newcastle, 1904.
Irish International Exhibition, Dublin, 1907.

References

Art Journal, 1887, pp. 246, 349.
Magazine of Art, 1887, Vol. X, p. 384.
The Illustrated London News, May 7, 1887, p. 517.
Magazine of Art, 1888, Vol. X, reproduced on frontispiece.
A. G. Temple, *The Art of Painting in the Queen's Reign*, London, 1897, pp. 200-201.
Sir Cuthbert Quilter's Pictures, London, n.d., p. 87, reproduced facing p. 87.
"John William Waterhouse, RA: His Life and Work," *Art Annual: Supplement to the Art Journal*, 1909, reproduced p. 24.
Muriel Freeman, "Kinetic Art in the Forbes Collection," *New Jersey Music & Arts* September, 1974, reproduced p. 35 (see gallery view, upper right corner).
"Das Glück kam spat, aber dann kam es reichlich," *Quick*. September 5-11, 1974, reproduced p. 81 (see gallery view, upper left corner).

Forthcoming References

Anthony Hobson is working on a book on J. W. Waterhouse.

66. J. W. Waterhouse, *Mariamne*.
(*see color Plate XXIV, p. 182*)

GEORGE FREDERIC WATTS, RA
(1817-1904)

was born in London on February 27, 1817. As a child he suffered from ill health and did not go to school. He frequented the studio of the sculptor William Behnes and attended the Royal Academy Schools for a short time, but he was largely self-taught as an artist. In 1837 he first exhibited at the Royal Academy, and in 1843 he won a first prize in the initial cartoon competition for the Houses of Parliament (see Appendix II). With his prize money he set off for Italy, where he became the guest of Lord Holland, the British Minister to the Court of Tuscany. He remained in Florence until 1847, returning to England in that year to win another prize in the Parliament competitions. During the following few years, he painted his first major allegorical picture, *Of Time and Oblivion* as well as four large realistic pictures. In 1851 he met Mrs. Thoby Prinsep, and for the next quarter of a century he was the Prinseps' permanent guest at Little Holland House in Kensington. The Prinseps kept a semi-bohemian salon with Watts the genius in residence; the photographer Julia Margaret Cameron was Mrs. Prinsep's sister, and among their regular guests were Tennyson, Thackery, and Gladstone.

In 1852 Watts offered to decorate Euston Station with frescoes, without pay, but he was turned down; he did, however, between 1853 and 1859 paint a large fresco of *Justice* in the New Hall of Lincoln's Inn. For the rest of his life he occupied himself with painting portraits and large allegorical pictures. Watts was the leading portraitist of the Victorian era and his pictures of the eminent of the day provide a record which is often frightening in its penetration. His allegories were among the most ambitious works of the Victorian period. Watts was like Tennyson in wanting to express great truths at a time when science had undermined inherited beliefs. If what they found to say no longer seems entirely compelling, it was nonetheless said in richly lyrical language. Watts's earlier works after his Italian trip were strongly influenced by Titian; his later ones have a subtle delicacy of color, which by the end of his life became quite abstract. After 1870 he was also active as a sculptor.

During the 1850s Watts remained outside of the Royal Academy, but in 1867 he was elected an Associate Academician and an Academician in the same year. In 1864 he married Ellen Terry, then aged sixteen, but they separated the year after. In the 1880s and 1890s his reputation was enormous; he had one-man exhibitions at the Grosvenor Gallery in 1882 and at The Metropolitan Museum of Art in 1884-85. He twice declined a baronetcy. After 1875, when Little Holland House was demolished, Watts lived at

various places, eventually settling with his second wife at Limnerslease, Compton, Surrey, which became a museum after his death on July 1, 1904. During his career he exhibited one hundred and forty-five works at the Royal Academy and in the winter of 1905 there was a large retrospective exhibition there.

Bibliography

G. K. Chesterton, *G. F. Watts*, London, 1904.
Mrs. Russell Barrington, *G. F. Watts: Reminiscences,* London, 1905.
M. S. Watts, *George Frederic Watts: The Annals of the Artist's Life,* 3 Vols., London, 1912.
Ronald Chapman, *The Laurel and the Thorn: A Study of G. F. Watts,* London, 1945.
David Loshak, *George Frederic Watts, 1817-1904,* The Arts Council of Great Britain, 1954 (exhibition catalogue).
John Gage and Chris Mullen, *G. F. Watts: A Nineteenth Century Phenomenon,* The Whitechapel Art Gallery, London, 1974 (exhibition catalogue).

67. * ORPHEUS AND EURYDICE

Oil on canvas: 12-3/4 x 21 inches

This is one of eight canvases by Watts of the legend of Orpheus and Eurydice. Other versions are in the Walker Art Gallery, Liverpool, the Art Gallery, Aberdeen and the Watts Gallery, Compton Guilford. Of all versions this is the most intimate and sensual. The small size of the canvas allowed Watts to select a particularly touching moment in the legend. In Watts's other conceptions, Orpheus seizes the dying Eurydice round the waist in an heroic effort to prevent her from falling back into the Underworld, but here he lays his hand on her breast in a gesture reminiscent of Rembrandt's *Jewish Bride* (Rijksmuseum) suggesting infinite tenderness and pity. Orpheus seems to bid farewell to his lost Eurydice and makes no attempt to rescue his bride who is already dead. The painting was done in 1869 and shown at the Academy in May of the same year, along with Watts's *Return of the Dove to the Ark* (Buscot Park). In its review of the Academy Exhibition, the *Art Journal* wrote: "The high art and the grand style which have long obtained favour from Mr. Watts reached their best result in the lovely and rapturous composition *Orpheus and Eurydice*. The composition is studious of balanced lines, the forms are of noble type, the action is grand, even tragic. The work may be quoted as a striking example of how greatness may be made compatible with a small scale." Two letters exist about this picture. In the first dated 27th February 1869, Watts wrote to Mrs. Wyndham to tell her the price of the painting. On 1st May, the day the Exhibition opened, Gladstone wrote

to Watts to ask if it was for sale. The picture was sold to Watts's friends, the Wyndhams of Clouds, the house built for them by Philip Webb in 1881. There is a mezzotint of this picture by Frank Short.

Provenance

The Rt. Hon. Percy Wyndham
The Rt. Hon. George Wyndham
Mrs. Guy Wyndham
Christopher Gibbs Ltd., London

Exhibitions

Royal Academy, 1869, No. 700.
Works by the Late George Frederick Watts, Winter Exhibition, Royal Academy, 1905, No. 75.
Paintings in England, Christopher Gibbs, Ltd., 1973, No. 17 (reproduced in catalogue).

References

Art Journal, 1869, p. 201.
Hugh MacMillan, *The Life-Work of George Frederic Watts, RA,* London, 1903, pp. 109-113, reproduced opposite p. 110.
G. K. Chesterton, *G. F. Watts*, London, 1904, p. 44.
Mrs. Russell Barrington, *G. F. Watts: Reminiscences,* London, 1905, p. 63.
Masters in Art, A Series of Illustrated Monographs: Watts, Boston, 1905, pp. 21, 40-41, reproduced p. 21.
Masterpieces of G. F. Watts, Nineteenth Century Art Books, No. I, New York, n.d., reproduced p. 60.
G. F. Watts, Newnes' Art Library, London and New York, n.d., reproduced p. 63.

G. F. Watts, *Orpheus and Eurydice*

67. G. F. Watts, *Orpheus and Eurydice.*

THOMAS WEBSTER, RA
(1800-1886)

was born in 1800, the son of a member of the household of George III. His father desired that he become a musician and until after the death of George III in 1820, young Webster sang in the Royal choir. With the help of Henry Fuseli (1741-1825), he was able to gain entry to the Royal Academy Schools in 1820. Three years later he made his debut at the Academy's Summer Exhibition with *Portraits of Mr. Robinson and Family.* The following year, he won a Gold Medal in the Academy Schools. In 1827, a work exhibited at the British Institution, entitled *Rebels Shooting a Prisoner,* a mock-heroic incident in which little boys were depicted executing a doll with a toy canon, was very favorably received by the critics and general public alike. This acclaim determined Webster to paint works in the same vein throughout his career. Children's parodies, as popularized by Webster, became a minor genre in their own right, with numerous artists including Frederick Daniel Hardy (1826-1911), Charles Hunt (q.v.) and Matthais Robinson (q.v.) executing works in the same vein.

Webster, however, did not confine his inspiration to children; he also painted sympathetic scenes of contemporary rustic life of the type by which Sir David Wilkie (q.v.) successfully launched his own career in the early 1800s. Both artists looked to the Dutch genre painters of the seventeenth century, then much in vogue with British collectors, for their inspiration. Out of the resultant minutely detailed, carefully finished scenes of domestic life emerged the characteristic style of much Victorian genre painting.

Webster became an Associate of the Royal Academy in 1840 and six years later was elevated to the rank of full Academician. He stopped exhibiting at the Academy in 1879, having shown some eighty-three works over a period of fifty-three years. In 1856, he moved to Cranbrook, Kent where until his death thirty years later, he was the senior member of an artistic community known as the Cranbrook Colony (see Appendix I).

Bibliography

"British Artists: Their Style and Character; No. X — Thomas Webster, RA," *Art Journal,* 1855. pp. 293-296.
Richard Redgrave and Samuel Regrave, *A Century of Painters of the English School,* 2nd. ed., London, 1883, pp. 191-197.
Christopher Wood, *The Dictionary of Victorian Painters,* London, 1971, pp. 186-187.

68. A VILLAGE CHOIR

Watercolor: 22-1/2 x 34-1/4 inches
Original frame

The original painting of *A Village Choir* (Victoria and Albert Museum), of which this watercolor is a later replica, was commissioned by the prominent Victorian patron of the arts John Sheepshanks. It was inspired by a passage from *The Sketch Book* by Washington Irving which was quoted in the Royal Academy catalogue when the painting was exhibited there in 1847.

> 'If you are disposed to go to church,' said Frank Bracebridge, 'I can promise you a specimen of my cousin Simon's musical achievements. As the church is destitute of an organ he has formed a band from the village amateurs, and established a musical club for their improvement; he has also sorted a choir as he sorted my father's pack of hounds, according to the direction of Jervaise Markham, in his Country Contentment; for the bass he has sought out all the deep solemn mouths, and for the tenor the loud ringing mouths, among the country bumpkins.'

As in many of Webster's pictures, we see the gently humorous depiction of the varying attitudes of a group of people participating in a common activity. The artist's delineation of quaint or amusing characters drawn from different ranks of the community corresponds not only to his source in Washington Irving's *Sketch Book* but also to a major component of the early novels of Charles Dickens.

A Village Choir received enthusiastic reviews. The critic for *The Illustrated London News*

declared it "a most admirable picture. . . . One cannot commend too highly the extreme care with which every part is painted — care well bestowed, when such a picture is the result" (May 8, 1847, p. 296). In the *Art Union,* the reviewer described it as "admirable," especially the many figures "which exhibit that great merit — a decided diversity of character." However, the writer of this same review ended with the comment, "If we compare the picture with Webster's preceding works in which children are the actors, the preference will be given undoubtedly to the latter" (1847, p. 188).

In a biographical sketch on Webster, which appeared eight years later in the *Art Journal. A Village Choir* was described as being "full of humorous incident, carried out with the careful execution which has always distinguished the style of this painter" (1855, pp. 295-296).

Provenance

Anon. Sale: Christie's, London, June 12, 1973, Lot 238.
Fine Art Society, London (Agents).

Exhibitions

The Art and Mind of Victorian England: Paintings from the Forbes Magazine Collection, University Gallery, University of Minnesota, Minneapolis, 1974, No. 44 (reproduced in catalogue).

References

Lyndel King, "Heroism began at home," *Art News,* November, 1974, p. 45.
"Sing out the good News," *Forbes* November 1, 1974, p. 65, November 15, p. 125, December 1, p. 85, reproduced in color in each (advertisement).

T. Webster, *A Village Choir*
(Victoria and Albert Museum, London)

68. T. Webster, *A Village Choir*.

SIR DAVID WILKIE, RA
(1785-1841)

was born in 1785, the son of a Scottish minister and the grandson of a miller from Cults, just north of Edinburgh. He first studied at the Trustees Academy in Edinburgh and began his professional career as an itinerant portrait painter in Scotland. In 1805 he moved to London where his pictures of Scottish rural life, such as the first work he sent to the Academy, *The Village Politicans* exhibited in 1806, were enormously popular and brought him to the attention of rich and powerful patrons, including the Prince Regent, for whom he painted two of his most beautiful early works, *Blind Man's Buff* and *The Penny Wedding*. Wilkie was elected an Associate Academician in 1809 and a full Academician in 1811. In 1823, following the death of Sir Henry Raeburn (1756-1823), he was appointed King's Limner for Scotland. He was Painter in Ordinary to William IV and to Queen Victoria, and he was knighted in 1836.

In 1825 Wilkie began an extended trip to Italy and Spain, where he saw paintings by Correggio, Velasquez, and Murillo. His earlier genre paintings had been strongly influenced by the small scale and precise detail of seventeenth-century Dutch and Flemish genre painters such as David Teniers, but after his trip he began to paint more broadly on a larger scale in emulation of the Spanish and Italian masters he had studied. He also expanded his range of subject matter, painting most notably a number of pictures based on contemporary recent history. However, this development actually began before his travels; his most successful painting of a contemporary subject was *Chelsea Pensioners Receiving the London Gazette Extraordinary of Thursday, June 22nd 1815, Announcing the Battle of Waterloo!!!* (Apsley House, London) which he painted for the Duke of Wellington and exhibited at the Royal Academy in 1822. This painting was so popular that it was the first and, until William Powell Frith (q.v.) exhibited his *Derby Day* in 1858, the only painting in the history of the Academy for which a guard rail had to be constructed to protect it from the pressure of the crowds. The artist's later works, although more ambitious, were less widely popular.

Wilkie traveled abroad again in 1840, visiting Constantinople and the Near East in order to see the places where the events described in the Bible had taken place. He died at sea on the return voyage in 1841, and the following summer four pictures including a *Portrait of the Sultan Abdul Meedgid* were the last of some ninety-nine works by Wilkie to be shown in the Academy's annual exhibitions of contemporary art. A memorial exhibition of his works was held at the British Institution in 1842.

Bibliography

Works of Sir David Wilkie, RA, Christie's, London, 25-30, April 1842 (sale catalogue).
Sir David Wilkie's Sketches in Turkey, Syria and Egypt, 1840 and 1841, London, 1843.
Allan Cunningham, *The Life of Sir David Wilkie*, 3 Vols., London, 1843.
"British Artists: Their Style and Character; No. XXXIX —Sir David Wilkie, RA," *Art Journal*, 1858, pp. 301-303.
Works of Sir David Wilkie, RA, Christie's, London, 20-21 June 1860 (sale catalogue).
Lord Ronald Sutherland Gower, *Sir David Wilkie*, London, 1902.
Ramsay, Raeburn and Wilkie, Arts Council of Great Britain, Scottish Committee, Edinburgh, 1951 (exhibition catalogue).
John Woodward, *Paintings and Drawings by Sir David Wilkie*, National Gallery of Scotland, Edinburgh and Royal Academy, 1958 (exhibition catalogue).

69. * SANCHO PANZA IN THE DAYS OF HIS YOUTH

Oil on panel: 24 x 19-3/4 inches
Inscribed, middle right: *David Wilkie / 1835*
Original frame

When *Sancho Panza in the Days of his Youth* or *Girl at the Well*, as it has also been called, was exhibited at the Royal Academy in 1835, the title was followed in the catalogue by the following quotation from *Don Quixote*: "Aqua limpia a la Oveja, y Vino rubio para el Rey respondio Sancho" meaning "Clean water for the sheep, white wine for the King, answered Sancho."

This painting is one of very few works exhibited by Wilkie which were based on literary sources. It does not illustrate a scene from *Don Quixote* in elaborate detail as does Charles Robert Leslie's *Sancho Panza in the Apartment of the Duchess* (see No. 39) but rather transforms the subject into a graceful genre scene. Sancho Panza was perhaps the most popular of all literary figures with the Victorians, so even this less-well-known moment outside the main action of Cervantes's picaresque novel would have been readily recognizable and of interest and appeal to the exhibition-going public. The great popularity of scenes of childhood by Wilkie and his many imitators was based on the Victorians' conviction of the profound importance of upbringing in shaping the character of the mature man; and what could be more interesting than an incident from the formative years of a character as memorable as Sancho Panza?

Wilkie had visited Spain less than a decade before he painted this picture, and his visualiza-

tion was no doubt based on memories of what he had seen there. The flowing composition, the painterly handling, and the rich use of color all reflect his ambition to develop an old-masterly style based on artists such as Velasquez and Murillo.

Provenance

John M. Naylor, Leighton Hall, Welshpool (Sale: Christie's, London, February 19, 1923, Lot 47).
Anon Sale: Christie's, London, July 14, 1972, Lot 156, reproduced.
Fine Art Society, London (Agents).

Exhibitions

Royal Academy, 1835, No. 127.
Painting and Drawings by Sir David Wilkie, RA, National Gallery of Scotland, Edinburgh and Royal Academy, 1958, No. 70.
The Art and Mind of Victorian England: Paintings from the Forbes Magazine Collection, University Gallery, University of Minnesota, Minneapolis, 1974, No. 45 (reproduced in catalogue).

References

Allan Cunningham, *The Life Of Sir David Wilkie*, London, 1843, Vol. III, p. 45.
Lord Ronald Sutherland Gower, FSA, *Great Masters in Painting and Sculpture: Sir David Wilkie*, London, 1902, p. 96.
Masters in Art, A Series of Illustrated Monographs: Sir David Wilkie, Boston, 1906, p. 335.
"Victorian Art and Mind," *Apollo*, December 1974, p. 257.

69. D. Wilkie, *Sancho Panza in the Days of His Youth.*

ALMA-TADEMA, NO. 1
(continued from page 20)

1885, the central couple provided the inspiration for a life-size sculpture by Thomas Nelson Maclean (1845-1894).

Provenance

Pilgeram and Lefevre, London, purchased from the artist July 24, 1879.

British Galleries, London

Anne W. Penfield, Philadelphia (Sale: American Art Association, New York, May 18, 1934, Lot 87, reproduced).

Guilford Hall, Palm Beach

Newhouse Galleries, New York

Exhibitions

Berlin Academy, 1879.

The Hague, November, 1879.

Royal Academy, 1880, No. 176.

Grosvenor Gallery, 1880.

Salon, Paris, 1881, No. 22.

Victorian Art, The Emily Lowe Gallery, Hofstra University, Hempstead, New York, 1972, No. 58.

References

Art Journal, 1880, p. 187.

Henry Blackburn, *Academy Notes,* London, 1880, p. 22, reproduced, p. 22.

Magazine of Art, 1880, Vol. III, p. 316, reproduced p. 316.

The Illustrated London News, May 1, 1880, p. 435.

Catalogne Illustré de Salon de 1881, Paris, 1881, p. 190, reproduced.

Frederick G. Stephens, *Artists at Home,* New York, 1884, p. 32.

The Illustrated London News, June 27, 1885, p. 648.

Percy Cross Standing, *Sir Lawrence Alma-Tadema, OM, RA,* London, 1905, p. 69.

Rudolf Dircks, "The Later Works of Sir Lawrence Alma-Tadema," *Art Annual: Supplement to The Art Journal,* 1910, p. 31.

The Art Quarterly, Autumn, 1970, reproduced (Newhouse Advertisement).

Michael A. Findlay, "Forbes Saves the Queen," *Arts Magazine,* February, 1973, p. 27, reproduced p. 28

Forthcoming References

Charles Spencer, *Alma-Tadema,* Academy Editions, London and St. Martin's Press, New York, November-December, 1975, to be reproduced (tentative title, publishers and publication dates).

Vern Swanson, *Alma-Tadema, Great Painter, Brave Worker, Strong Friend,* a catalogue raisonné, 1975, catalogue op. 208, to be reproduced (publishers and exact date of publication to be determined).

DYCE, NO. 11
(continued from page 40)

of the Queen of England. In the sketch we see Britannia standing on the shore accompanied by her lion and figures emblematic of Britain's intellectual, agricultural, and industrial accomplishments. Britannia already holds Neptune's trident, and Mercury is about to pass her the crown proffered by the god of the sea. Neptune is accompanied by Amphitrite; Tritons blow a fanfare on conch shells; and three mermaids offer riches from the deep. The composition is a symbolic representation of the maritime supremacy which Britain maintained throughout the nineteenth century.

On January 13, 1847 Dyce told his fellow artist Charles West Cope (1811-1890) that his sketch had been most graciously received: "Prince thought it rather nude; the Queen, however, said not at all, He stayed to lunch and is to begin it as soon as possible." Three days later Cope saw the sketch: "clever and agreeable, in the style of Raffaelle's *Galatea;* Britannia too rustic." Dyce traveled to the Isle of Wight in July 1847 and spent two months, from August 3 to October 7, painting the actual fresco, which is approximately ten feet high by seventeen feet wide. He was paid £800. Apart from a bare leg on a more commanding and less "rustic" Britannia, some changes in hair styles and the addition of dramatic clouds in the sky, there are no major compositional changes between the sketch and the finished fresco. According to a letter written by Dyce to Cope in August, "The nurserymaids and French governesses have been sadly scandalized by the nudities, . . . but I think they have now become accustomed to the sight." In a slightly earlier letter he advised Cope:

> when you are about to paint a sky seventeen feet long by some four or five broad, I don't advise you to have a Prince looking in upon you every ten minutes or so — or when you are going to trace an outline to obtain the assistance of the said Prince and an Archduke Constantine to hold up your tracing to the wall, as I have had. It is very polite, condescending, and so forth, very amusing to Princes and Dukes, but rather embarrassing to the artist.

When the sketch was exhibited at the Royal Academy, the critical reception which greeted it was mixed. The *Art Union* described it as

> brilliant in colour, and original in style; the narrative is so perspicuous as to require no descriptive title; and it is more probable that, on a larger scale, the composition will acquire yet higher qualities.

In *The Illustrated London News,* on the other hand, the critic, while describing the "general composition" as "extremely careful" and "the colouring . . . warm and truthful," went on to declare:

> The figure of Britannia is a failure — she is a silly country lass: —
>
> O, silly I; more silly than my sheep.
>
> Her lion, too, is a sorry representation of the monarch of the forest.

The naked figure holding a caduceus and wearing a Phrygian cap was the subject of a lengthy parody in *Punch* entitled "A Chance for High Art," in which the imaginary writer of a letter argues that figures in allegorical compositions such as Dyce's should be clothed in contemporary dress (1847, pp. 218-219).

This sketch was executed at midpoint in Dyce's career. Although he was to be one of the original supporters of the Pre-Raphaelites, Dyce demonstrated in this work that his enthusiasm for Italian art was not confined to the fifteenth century. As Cope recognized in 1847, the composition recalls Raphael's *Galatea* in the Villa Farnesina in Rome, a building to which Osborne House is comparable architecturally. Dyce's work is also strongly reminiscent of the *Triumph of Neptune and Amphitrite* (Philadelphia Museum of Art) by Nicholas Poussin, an artist for whom he had always professed admiration. The Poussin was in Russia from 1771 to 1930, but there were two copies of it in England in the nineteenth century as well as engravings which Dyce could have known. In Dyce's next major work, the frescoes of Arthurian subjects in the Queen's Robing Room in the Palace of Westminster, which were commissioned in the summer of 1847 and begun the following year, he employed a more archaizing style.

Provenance

H. M. Queen Victoria, presented by Prince Albert who commissioned the picture, Windsor Castle Inventory, 1872, No. 647, Queen's Personal Property.

Prince Arthur, Duke of Connaught

Princess Victoria Patricia, Lady Ramsay, Ribsden Holt, Windlesham Surrey (Sale: Christie's, London, July 26, 1974, No. 252, reproduced).

Thomas Agnew & Sons, London.

Exhibitions

Royal Academy, 1847, No. 42.

William Dyce, RA (1806-1864), Aberdeen Art Gallery and Thomas Agnew & Sons, London, 1964, No. 25.

Victorian Artists in England, National Gallery of Canada, Ottawa, 1965, No. 30.

References

Art Union, 1847, p. 186.

The Illustrated London News, May 8, 1847, p. 297.

James Dafforne, "British Artists: Their Style and Character: William Dyce, RA," *Art Journal*, 1860, p. 296.

Robert Brydall, *Art in Scotland: Its Origin and Progress*, Edinburgh and London, 1889, p. 402.

Charles Henry Cope, *Reminiscences of Charles West Cope, RA, by His Son*, London, 1891, pp. 167, 171-173.

James Stirling Dyce, "The Life, Correspondence, and Writing of William Dyce, RA, 1806-1864," unpublished typescript by Dyce's son in the Aberdeen Art Gallery, pp. 870, 973.

HALSWELLE, NO. 21
(*continued from page 58*)

"Our own Academy Guide: Positively the Last Visit," *Punch*, June 15, 1878, p. 265.

Clara Clement and Lawrence Hutton, *Artists of the Nineteenth Century*, London, 1879, p. 326.

James Dafforne, "The Works of Keeley Halswelle, ARSA," *Art Journal*, 1879, p. 52.

W. W. Fenn, "Keeley Halswelle, ARSA," *Magazine of Art*, Vol. IV, 1881, p. 410.

LESLIE, NO. 39
(*continued from page 94*)

Don Quixote and his squire have been invited into the castle of a duke and duchess, and in the scene shown Sancho is having an interview with the duchess while his master naps. As a servant and member of the lower classes, he sits uncomfortably, and he lays his finger alongside his nose to indicate that his revelations about his master are made in strictest confidence. The grim-visaged woman to the left of the duchess is the duenna, Doña Rodriguez, whom Sancho had insulted in a previous chapter by asking her to care for his mount.

The composition is the same in all four versions of the picture, but the details of decoration and costume, and of the individual figures, vary in each. For the first version, Leslie used furniture and decorations at Petworth as props; the sculptor Sir Francis Chantrey (1781-1842) sat for the figure of Sancho Panza. Leslie exhibited his second version of the subject at the Royal Academy in 1844. It was painted for Robert Vernon, who presented it to the National Gallery in 1847, and is now in the Tate Gallery, where there is also a small oil sketch for the picture. The third version was painted for the poet Samuel Rogers, and in his sale at Christie's in 1856, sold for 1,150 gns. This version was sold again at Sotheby's Belgravia on March 27, 1973 (Lot 58).

When the second version of the picture was exhibited at the Royal Academy in 1844 the critic for the *Art Union* remarked:

> such are the scenes in which the artist excels. . . . in paintings from Shakespere [sic] he is unequal; but his readings from Cervantes and Molière are unrivalled. We cannot therefore, in this instance, regret that he has gone over familiar ground. The composition of the picture has undergone several very striking improvements — a consequence of renewed consideration; and the style is comparatively free from the cold chalky colour, which impairs so many of the painter's recent works — result of his profound worship of the manner of Constable (p. 161).

For a different visualization of Sancho Panza, see No. 69.

Provenance

Painted for the artist's sister
John Farnworth, by 1860, (Sale: Christie's London, May 19, 1874, Lot 87, £ 745 10s).
The Cooling Galleries, London
Mr. Mitchell, Kensington
Anon. Sale: Christie's, January 28, 1972, Lot 79.
Fine Art Society, London (Agents).

Exhibitions

The Art and Mind of Victorian England: Paintings from the Forbes Magazine Collection, University of Minnesota, Minneapolis, 1974, No. 30 (reproduced in catalogue).

References

Tom Taylor, ed. *Autobiographical Recollections by the late Charles Robert Leslie, RA, with a Prefatory Essay on Leslie as an Artist*, and *Selections from his Correspondence*, London, 1860, Vol. I, p. xxix.

Allan Cunningham, *Lives of the Most Eminent British Painters*, London, 1879-1880, Vol. III, p. 350 (revised edition, annotated and continued to the time by Mrs. Charles Heaton).

MILLAIS, NO. 45
(*continued from page 106*)

embroidered sleeve which peeps out from under his disguise.

According to Effie Millais (quoted by J. G. Millais), the idea for the picture occurred on a visit to Sir William Stirling (1818-1878; he is better known by the hyphenated name Stirling-Maxwell, which he adopted in 1865) at Keir House, near Dunblane in Scotland. Stirling was a historian and art-historian (his history of Spanish painting was the source for *The Early Career of Murillo* by John Phillip [See No. 52]), and he owned a collection of books about the Spanish Inquisition which he had used in writing *The Cloister Life of Emperor Charles V*, published in 1852. The model for the lover, who looks more like a Scottish gillie than a Spanish grandee, was the gamekeeper of a Mr. Condie. The setting is based on the staircase of Dalhousie (misprinted in J. G. Millais as Balhousie) Castle near Edinburgh. For the costumes Millais used engravings of monks of different orders and the habit of a Carthusian from the Papal states, which he borrowed from a friend.

Millais conceived *The Escape of a Heretic, 1559* as a pendant to *A Hugenot on St. Bartholomew's Day Refusing to Shield Himself from Danger by Wearing the Roman Catholic Badge* (Private Collection, Great Britain), which he had exhibited at the Royal Academy in 1852. It is one of a series of pictures which Millais painted repeating the *Hugenot's* formula of a pair of historical lovers one of whom is saving or trying to save the other. The series includes *The Proscribed Royalist, 1651* (Private Collection, Great Britain) and *The Order of Release, 1746* (Tate Gallery), both exhibited the year after the *Hugenot*, and *The Black Brunswicker* (Lady Lever Art Gallery, Port Sunlight), which Millais exhibited in 1860. Like the Protestant lover in the *Hugenot*, the heroine in *The Escape of a Heretic* is threatened with execution by militant Roman Catholics, and although Millais was probably drawn to both subjects because they provide evocative settings for moving and dramatic incidents, his interest in such themes also reflects traditional English Protestant hostility to the Catholic Church. Millais's first exhibited picture, *Pizarro Seizing the Inca of Peru*, shown at the Royal Academy in 1846 (Victoria and Albert Museum), depicted a monk waving a crucifix on high while encouraging Spanish soldiers to kill Indians, and in later years he returned to sword-wielding Catholics in pictures such as *"Mercy": St. Bartholomew's Day, 1572* (Tate Gallery), which he exhibited in 1887.

The picture was greeted by a torrent of unfavorable reviews including one by John Ruskin, who led off, "The conception . . . is an example of the darkest error in judgement — the fatalest failure in the instinct of the painter's mind. At once coarse and ghastly in fancy, exaggerated and obscure in action . . ." (*Works*, Vol. XIV, pp. 110-111). He continued in the same vein for a few hundred more words. Determined to ignore the criticism, Millais declared in a letter to his wife, "The public crowd around my pictures more than ever, and this, I think is the main cause of animosity" (J. G. Millais, Vol. I, p. 323). Millais would continue to appeal more to the crowd and less to his former Pre-Raphaelite brothers and supporters.

The small replica of *The Escape of a Heretic* was commissioned in 1857 by the dealer Ernest Gambart, who commissioned two small replicas of the *Huguenot* in the same year.

Provenance

Ernest Gambart

Thomas Plint (Sale: Christie's, London, March 8, 1862, Lot 296)

F. J. Pilgeram

A granddaughter of William Tarn (Sale: Christie's London, December 15, 1972, Lot 115, reproduced)

J. S. Maas & Co., Ltd., London

Fine Art Society, London (Agents).

Exhibition

The *Pre-Raphaelite Influence*, Maas Gallery, London, 1973, No. II.

References

M. H. Speilmann, *Millais and His Works*, London 1898, pp. 169, 183.

John Guille Millais, *The Life and Letters of Sir John Everett Millais*, New York, 1899, Vol. II, p. 470.

ORCHARDSON, NO. 51

(continued from page 116)

Islands in the seventeenth century to a well-mannered party of figures tastefully garbed in late eighteenth-century costume. This picture was the last of Orchardson's paintings of literary subjects based on Scott and Shakespeare, and the first of a series of pictures of refined social life in eighteenth-century and Regency settings.

The painting was greeted by universal critical acclaim when it was first shown at the Royal Academy in 1877 and Orchardson was elected a full Academician. When it was exhibited in Paris in the following year, one critic very much admired the demeanor of the young Queen but decried the looseness of the handling. Walter Sickert, writing in 1910, although he was an admirer of Orchardson cited *"The Queen of the Swords"* as an example of Orchardson's failure to control the space in crowded compositions: "His tableaux were set rather for the stage than for canvas. Painters will understand me when I say that the furthest figures in them made holes in the wall that was supposed to be behind them."

Provenance

J. G. Sandeman, Glasgow

The French Galleries, London and New York

Mrs. Robert W. Paterson, Clarendon Hotel, New York

David David, Inc., Philadelphia

Frederick Thom Gallery, Toronto

Exhibitions

Royal Academy, 1877, No. 174.

Exposition Universelle, Paris, 1878, No. 191.

Royal Scottish Academy, 1879, No. 251.

Royal Glasgow Institute, 1882, No. 33.

Edinburgh, 1886, No. 1689.

Earls Court, 1897.

Glasgow, 1911.

On loan to the Brooklyn Institute of Arts, 1920-1922.

Sir William Quiller Orchardson RA, The Scottish Arts Council, Edinburgh, 1972, No. 27 (reproduced in color in catalogue).

The Art and Mind of Victorian England: Paintings from the Forbes Magazine Collection, University Gallery, University of Minnesota, Minneapolis, 1974, No. 38 (reproduced in catalogue).

References

Art Journal, 1877, p. 199.

Athenaeum, Vol. I, 1877, p. 646.

Henry Blackburn, *Academy Notes*, London, 1877, pp. 21-22, reproduced.

The Illustrated London News, May 19, 1877, p. 474.

Henry Blackburn, *An Illustrated Catalogue of Painting and Sculpture in the British Fine Art Section, Universal Exhibition*, Paris, 1878, p. 39, reproduced p. 39.

Magazine of Art, Vol. I, 1878, p. 127, reproduced.

Edward Strahan, ed., *The Chefs–d'oeuvre d'art of the International Exhibition*, Philadelphia, 1878, p. 92, reproduced facing p. 92.

Magazine of Art, Vol. IV, 1881, p. 228, reproduced.

Walter Armstrong, *Scottish Painters*, London, 1888, p. 86.

Art Journal, 1894, pp. 34, 60.

Walter Armstrong, *The Art of William Quiller Orchardson*, London, 1895, pp. 29, 30, 35, 40.

James Stanly Little, "The Life and Work of William Q. Orchardson, RA," *Art Annual: Supplement of the Art Journal*, 1897, pp. 23-24, reproduced p. 23.

Scribner's Magazine, April, 1897, p. 406.

A. G. Temple, *The Art of Painting in the Queen's Reign*, London, 1897, p. 306.

Cosmo Monkhouse, *British Contemporary Artists*, New York, 1899, pp. 172-175.

Windsor Magazine, 1906, reproduced p. 23.

James L. Caw, *Scottish Painting, Past and Present 1620-1908*, Edinburgh, 1908, p. 237.

The Bulletin of the Brooklyn Institute of Arts, Vol. 24, December 25, 1920.

Masterpieces of Orchardson, London, 1913, reproduced p. 39.

Hilda Orchardson Gray, *The Life of William Quiller Orchardson, RA DCI, HRSA, PSPP*, London, 1930, pp. 12-96, 273, 351, reproduced opposite p. 80.

Walter R. Sickert, *A Free House*, O. Sitwell, ed., London, 1947, p. 72.

"Victorian Art and Mind," *Apollo*, December, 1974, p. 527.

PHILLIP, NO. 52

(continued from page 118)

R.A.M. Stevenson, "Mr. Kieller's Collection in Dundee," *Art Journal*, 1894, p. 58, reproduced p. 55.

A.G. Temple, *The Art of Painting in the Queen's Reign*, London, 1897, p. 136.

William D. McKay, *The Scottish School of Painting*, London, 1906, pp. 282, 288.

James L. Caw, *Scottish Painting, Past and Present 1620-1908*, Edinburg, 1908, p. 181.

Charles Carter, *John Phillip, RA*, Aberdeen Art Gallery, Aberdeen, 1967, p. 8 (exhibition catalogue).

Forthcoming References

David Robertson, *Sir Charles Eastlake and the Victorian Art World*, Princeton University Press, 1975 (?), Appendix E.3.

POTT, NO. 55

(continued from page 120)

writing in the *Art Journal* of 1874, while categorizing it "among the less important works," also noted:

> The broken line of soldiers, over-wearied and discouraged is set on the canvas with evident knowledge of the sources of strong effect. In general scheme and treatment the influence of the school of Dusseldorf is plainly visible.

The reviewer's reference to the influence of the school of Dusseldorf is interesting as one of the few suggestions of the influence of German art in England after the 1850s, but it is also puzzling. This picture of part of an army on the move in winter, in which each soldier is individually characterized rather than treated with military uniformity, does have at least superficial resemblance to the most famous of all Dusseldorf pictures, *Washington Crossing the Delaware* by Emanuel Leutze (1816-1868) in the Metropolitan Museum of Art. However, in the biographical account of Pott's life published by James Dafforne in the same periodical four years later, no mention is made of any study in Dusseldorf or of any other connection with German art. Dafforne was certainly not unaware of *On the March from Moscow*; on the contrary, he praised it as one of the artist's highest achievements — "We do not think the artist has ever surpassed this picture in genuine expression and strong appeal." — so he would have taken into account any direct German influence had he known of it. In Pott's later works such as *Napoleon's Farewell to Josephine*, exhibited in 1891, "genuine expression" is replaced by sentimentality.

Provenance

T. Smith

Anon. Sale: Christie's, London, November 20, 1970, Lot 287.

Anon. Sale: Christie's, London, July 28, 1972, Lot 413.

Exhibitions

Royal Academy, 1873, No. 337.

Nottingham, 1878, No. 174.

References

Art Journal, 1873, p. 198.

The Illustrated London News, May 17, 1873, p. 471.

James Dafforne, "The Works of Laslett John Pott," *Art Journal,* 1877, p. 259, reproduced.

REDGRAVE, NO. 58
(continued from page 124)

is as much, if not more, a microscopic rendering of natural detail than a scene from *Hamlet.* In the case of Redgrave's painting one only has to compare it to his own earlier depiction of a similar subject, *The Lost Path,* exhibited at the Royal Academy in 1853, to see the change in his art.

Redgrave seems to have been obsessed with the theme of children lost or wandering in the woods. In addition to *The Lost Path* of 1853, he also exhibited a *Little Red Riding Hood* in 1856, and in 1860 when he exhibited *The Children in the Wood—The Morning,* it accompanied another picture of *The Children in the Wood—The Evening.* Since Redgrave entitled these two pictures *The Children in the Wood,* and not *Babes in the Wood,* it seems unlikely that he intended them as illustrations to the nursery story which is generally known by the latter title (i.e. *Babes in the Wood* is the title of the show being performed in No. 4, *The Peepshow* by John Burr). As *The Children in the Wood—The Evening* is lost, we do not know what frightening things it may have shown, but here, in its sequel, the children are seen sleeping peacefully protected by the surrounding foliage, their innocence in harmony with the natural world. In the year that Redgrave painted this picture, Charles Darwin published *On the Origin of Species,* a work which soon was to engender a much tougher view of the natural order.

Provenance

J. S. Maas & Co., Ltd., London.

Exhibitions

Royal Academy, 1860, No. 238.

The Art and Mind of Victorian England: Paintings from the Forbes Magazine Collection, University Gallery, University of Minnesota, Minneapolis, 1974, No. 40 (reproduced in catalogue in color).

References

Art Journal, 1860, p. 167.

Frederick G. Stephens, *Artists at Home,* New York, 1884, p. 36.

Melvin Waldfogel, "Introduction," *The Art and Mind of Victorian England: Paintings from the Forbes Magazine Collection,* University Gallery, University of Minnesota, Minneapolis, 1974, p. 21 (exhibition catalogue).

Peter Altman, "Victorian age ideals evident in art works," *The Minneapolis Star,* September 28, 1974.

Lyndel King, "Heroism began at home," *Art News,* November, 1974, p. 45, reproduced in color p. 44.

APPENDIX I

THE CLIQUE

The Clique, whose membership included, according to various sources, Richard Dadd (1819-1887), William Powell Frith (q.v.), Henry Nelson O'Neil (q.v.), Augustus Leopold Egg (q.v.), John Phillip (q.v.), Edward Matthew Ward (q.v.), Alfred Elmore (1815-1881), and Thomas Joy (1812-1866), was a sketching society. It began to take shape in 1837, when Dadd, Phillip, and Frith entered the Royal Academy Schools, and it was essentially an informal student group. The young artists met one evening a week in Dadd's rooms where they spent one to two hours sketching incidents chosen chiefly from Byron or Shakespeare, after which one of the guests would choose the best rendering. Dadd, whose work was generally judged to be the finest, often did character portraits of the members and guests, which filled the walls of his studio. The evenings ended in a small repast of bread, cheese, and beer; and the meetings, themselves, came to an end in 1841 or early 1842 when Dadd received an important commission for a series of paintings for Lord Foley's town house in Grosvenor Square. Although several members of the group went on individually to have distinguished careers, in all cases their most distinctive contributions came at least a decade after The Clique's demise. The fullest account of the group by a contemporary witness is "A Reminiscence of Sixty Years Ago" by John Imray published in the *Art Journal* in 1898, p. 202.

THE PRE-RAPHAELITE BROTHERHOOD

The Pre-Raphaelite Brotherhood was founded in 1848 by three students in the Royal Academy Schools, John Everett Millais (q.v.), William Holman Hunt (q.v.), and Dante Gabriel Rossetti (1828-1882), in opposition to the current academic standards. Their ideals combined an interest in fifteenth-century art and an up-to-date desire to paint with exact realism. The former was reflected not only in their choice of a name for the group but also in the bright colors and linear style of their first pictures; the latter, in the microscopically precise detail which resulted from their laborious practice of painting all parts of their pictures directly from nature. William Michael Rossetti (1829-1919), James Collinson (q.v.), Frederick George Stephens (1828-1907), and Thomas Woolner (1825-1892) were also among the original seven members of the PRB, while Ford Madox Brown (1821-1893), Walter Howell Deverell (1827-1854), Arthur Hughes (1832-1915), Charles Allston Collins (1828-1873), and several other artists were more loosely associated with the group. John Ruskin (1819-1900) is often mentioned in connection with the PRB because his *Modern Painters* inspired the group's theories, and for many years he championed their art. Collinson left the Pre-Raphaelite Brotherhood in 1850 and by 1853 it was virtually defunct as an organized group, but the importance of the movement for virtually all later Victorian art was profound. For a guide to the extensive literature on the PRB see *Pre-Raphaelitism: A Bibliocritical Study* (Cambridge, Mass., 1965) by William E. Fredeman.

THE CRANBROOK COLONY

The Cranbrook Colony pivoted around Thomas Webster (q.v.) who resided in the village of Cranbrook in Kent from 1856 until 1886. The group, which included Webster's pupil Frederick Daniel Hardy (1826-1911), Augustus E. Mulready (d. 1886), George Bernard O'Neill (1828-1917), and John Callcott Horsley (q.v.), congregated in and around Cranbrook during the summer months. They all shared a common interest in painting simple, contemporary domestic genre pieces, often of children, following in the tradition of David Wilkie (q.v.).

THE ST. JOHN'S WOOD CLIQUE

The members of the St. John's Wood Clique, Philip Hermogenes Calderon (q.v.), John Evan Hodgson (q.v.), George Dunlop Leslie (1835-1921), H. Stacy Marks (1829-1898), George Adolphus Storey (q.v.), Frederick Walker (1840-1875), David Wilkie Wynfield (1837-1887) and William Frederick Yeames (1835-1918), lived, with the exception of Walker, in close proximity of one another in the London suburb of St. John's Wood during the 1860s and '70s. Each Saturday, they would rendezvous at a different member's home to draw a given subject. The session would end with the rigorous grilling of each artist's work, a ritual from which originated the group's badge—a miniature gridiron inscribed with the motto, 'Ever On Thee'. And then the group would turn to socializing. Although all except Wynfield were stalwart members of the Royal Academy, the neighbors' shared penchant for practical jokes and fun, rather than any shared artistic commitment, seems to have provided the group's chief bond.

MARGARET KELLY

Ms. Kelly is the Assistant Curator of the Forbes Magazine Collection.

APPENDIX II

THE HOUSES
OF PARLIAMENT

On October 16, 1843 the British Houses of Parliament were destroyed by fire. A new building to replace them, the present Houses of Parliament (or Palace of Westminster at it is also known), was designed by Sir Charles Barry and begun the following year. By 1841 construction was far enough along that a Commission, headed by Prince Albert, was appointed to supervise the decoration of the new building. The Commissioners decided that the interiors should be decorated with monumental frescoes, and they sponsored a series of competitions to select the artists. The first competition, in which the artists were asked to submit cartoons for frescoes illustrative of English history or literature, took place in 1843, and there were additional competitions in the following years. The first fresco actually painted was *The Baptism of Ethelbert* by William Dyce (q.v.) in the House of Lords, commissioned in 1845 and executed in 1846. During the next quarter of a century many leading artists, including George Frederic Watts (q.v.), John Callcott Horsley (q.v.), John Rogers Herbert (q.v.), and Edward Matthew Ward (q.v.), were employed in the new building. Most of the frescoes deteriorated rapidly, and many no longer exist. The most important which are still visible are the cycle of Arthurian subjects by Dyce in the Queen's Robing Room and two huge scenes of *The Meeting of Wellington and Blücher* and *The Death of Nelson* by Daniel Maclise (q.v.) in the Royal Gallery.

THE BUCKINGHAM PALACE
GARDEN PAVILION

In 1843 Prince Albert commissioned a group of artists to paint a series of frescoes in the lunettes of the octagonal central room of a garden pavilion in the grounds of Buckingham Palace. This was just before artists were to be selected to paint the frescoes in the new Houses of Parliament, and the garden pavilion was intended as a kind of trial run. The artists originally chosen were Clarkson Stanfield (1793-1867), Thomas Uwins (1782-1857), Sir William Ross (1794-1860), Sir Charles Eastlake (q.v.), Charles Robert Leslie (q.v.), Daniel Maclise (q.v.), Sir Edwin Landseer (q.v.), and William Etty (q.v.), a cross section of the leading reputations of the day. Etty was unable to cope with the medium of fresco, and in 1844, amidst considerable bitterness, his commission was taken away and given to William Dyce (q.v.). The subjects of the frescoes were to be from Milton's *Masque of Comus,* each artist illustrating a scene of his own choosing. The results were all reproduced in *The Decoration of the Garden Pavilion in the Grounds of Buckingham Palace* by Ludwig Gruner and Mrs. Anna Jameson, published in 1846. The actual frescoes no longer exist, as the pavilion fell into disrepair and was pulled down early in this century.

THE VICTORIAN SOCIETY SCHOLARSHIP FUND
INCORPORATED

Paintings are fortunate. In most cases they survive the buildings and rooms in which they were hung by their original owners. Victorian buildings on both sides of the Atlantic are particularly vulnerable to destruction, because Victorian architecture has only recently begun to be re-appreciated after over half a century of neglect and ridicule.

The Victorian Societies in America and Great Britain were established over a decade ago to help save some of the best examples of this exhuberant age. Both Societies realized that in order to be successful in their preservation efforts, they had to educate people in general and architects and builders in particular to appreciate the merits of outstanding Victorian buildings and in some cases their interiors.

In 1974 The Victorian Society Scholarship Fund was launched by the Victorian Societies in America and Great Britain to service this need. In addition to making it possible to study important Victorian buildings in America and Britain, scholarships will enable young architects from each country to take part in practical restoration, adaptation and preservation work in the other.

I hope very much that you will support this vital effort. In the United States all contributions are tax deductable.

Sincere thanks,

Christopher Forbes

Christopher Forbes

Please make checks payable to The Victorian Society Scholarship Fund and forward them to:
Mr. Christopher Forbes, Director
The Victorian Society Scholarship Fund
60 Fifth Avenue
New York, New York 10011

or

Mrs. Edward Fawcett, M.B.E., Secretary
The Victorian Society Scholarship Fund
29 Exhibition Road
London, SW7 2AS

PLATES

Plate I

1. L. Alma-Tadema, *Spring Festival.*

Plate II

6. J. Collinson, *To Let.*

Plate III

10. F. Dicksee, *Chivalry*.

Plate IV

11. W. Dyce, *Neptune Resigning to Britannia
the Empire of the Sea.*

Plate V

12. C. L. Eastlake, *The Salutation to the Aged Friar.*

Plate VI

14. W. Etty, *Phaedria and Cymochles on the Idle Lake.*

Plate VII

17. W. P. Frith, *'For Better, For Worse.'*

Plate VIII

24. J. R. Herbert, *The Monastery in the 14th Century;*
Boar-Hunters Refreshed at
St. Augustine's Monastery, Canterbury.

Plate IX

25. H. von Herkomer, *The First-Born.*

Plate X

30. W. H. Hunt, *Il Dolce Far Niente*.

Plate XI

33. E. Landseer, *Queen Victoria's
Favorite Dogs and Parrot.*

Plate XII

37. F. Leighton, *Bacchante*.

Plate XIII

40. J. F. Lewis, *The Street and Mosque of
the Ghoreeyah, Cairo*

Plate XIV

42. J. Linnell, *The Return of Ulysses*.

Plate XV

43. D. Maclise, *The·Play Scene in Hamlet*.

Plate XVI

45. J. E. Millais, *The Escape of a Heretic, 1559.*

Plate XVII

48. A. Moore, *A Flower Walk*.

Plate XVIII

50. H. N. O'Neil, *Eastward Ho! August 1857.*

Plate XIX

50. H. N. O'Neil, *Home Again — 1858.*

Plate XX

51. W. Q. Orchardson, *"The Queen of the Swords."*

Plate XXI

52. J. Phillip, *The Early Career of Murillo, 1634.*

Plate XXII

56. E. J. Poynter, *The Prodigal's Return*.

Plate XXIII

3. J. Brett, *Pearly Summer.*

60. D. Roberts, *View Showing the Entrance to the
Firth of Forth, with a Proposed Reconstruction
of the Temple of the Sibyl, at
Tivoli, on the Rock of Drumsapie,
near Queen's Drive, in Queen's Park, Edinburgh.*

Plate XXIV

66. J. W. Waterhouse, *Mariamne.*